6

DOUBLE TAKE

A Girl Photo Story

Orphan, Sandra Martin had been in hospital for six months. But when the doctors said she could go home, she was puzzled . . .

I JUST DON'T UNDERSTAND WHY THE DOCTORS LET ME OUT OF HOSPITAL. I DON'T FEEL ANY BETTER.

I'M SURE YOU WILL, LOVE.

WHEN YOU GET HOME YOU WILL, DEAR — I'M SURE.

I DO HOPE SO.

THESE LAST SIX MONTHS IN HOSPITAL HAVE SEEMED LIKE SIX YEARS. I THOUGHT I WAS NEVER GOING TO GET OUT.

GRAN — YOU'RE CRYING.

I'M JUST SO PLEASED YOU'RE COMING HOME, DEAR. THAT'S ALL.

And a few minutes later . . .

IT CAN'T HAVE BEEN EASY FOR GRAN AND GRANDAD EITHER. THEY BOTH LOOK SO WORRIED . . .

I'M GLAD I'LL BE SPENDING MY BIRTHDAY TOMORROW AT HOME. I THINK I'D HAVE CRIED ALL DAY IF I'D STILL BEEN IN HOSPITAL.

WELL, HERE WE ARE, AND NOTHING'S CHANGED. YOUR ROOM'S JUST THE SAME.

I'M SO HAPPY — IT'S MARVELLOUS TO BE HERE AGAIN.

£2.50

11

15

The End

ABBA

A Girl Pin-Up

When this lot aren't busy in the recording studio, they're usually to be found hard at work in the gym!

Bjorn plays tennis and he's also a keen runner. Agnetha doesn't race — she's happy just running through the beautiful Swedish forests near her home.

* * * *

Benny is another dedicated tennis player, while Frida is often to be found keeping fit at a jazz ballet class. Keep at it, you energetic lot!

20 Ways To Keep Mum Happy...

Playing happy families isn't always easy. Try our tips and see how you do...

1 Don't leave all the work to Mum. Give her a hand with the washing up sometimes.

2 Nobody likes to be taken for granted, so surprise Mum with a bunch of flowers or a box of chocs when you're feeling rich!

3 Try to keep your room tidy — after all, Mum looks after all the others — it's only fair.

4 Half the battle is keeping the peace ... so next time your kid brother gets on your nerves, try not to fight with him!

5 Get straight on with your homework when you get in, so Mum doesn't have to nag!

6 Next time Mum treats herself to a new dress, tell her how nice she looks in it.

7 Offer to make the Sunday lunch next weekend — it'll give Mum a break!

8 Be a bit considerate when you play your records. Mum doesn't like your kind of music, so keep the volume down a bit.

9 Let Mum watch the TV shows she enjoys — even if 'Crossroads' isn't your cup of tea!

10 Don't leave Mum to always clean out your pets and take the dog for a walk.

11 Wash the bath round after you've used it — it's a very good habit to get into and it only takes a minute!

12 Next time Mum creates a new meal, remember to thank her.

13 Don't laze about in your dressing gown on Saturday mornings. Get dressed and see what you can do to help.

14 Remember Mother's Day and her birthday!

15 Stop using Mum's perfume — save up and buy some of your own!

16 Go to bed when you're told and tell yourself how good the beauty sleep will be for you!

17 Tell Mum her hair looks smashing, even if the hairdresser's gone a bit scissor-happy...

18 If Mum's nice enough to let you have friends round — keep the noise down!

19 Don't leave wet swimming togs hanging around till they start smelling mouldy — rinse them out and hang on the line.

20 Give her a great big hug now and then to show her how much you care!

Be a Super Fit Miss!

Here's how to make the most of your appearance with just a little care and attention. It's all down to eating the right food and doing some fun exercises to get you in tip-top shape!

Hey, you out there eating the crisps and drinking the Coke!

If you want to look good and feel terrific, in-between munchies will have to stop!

We've got together these terrific tips on how to look good and feel like a million dollars.

EATING PROPERLY

Don't despair! We're not suggesting you've got to cut out all your favourite food and live on vitamin pills and fish for the rest of your life. But there is certainly a right and wrong way to eat.

Large chunks of cake, sweets, hamburgers, chips, choccie bars and sweet, fizzy drinks may taste delicious, but they must not be the main part of your diet.

Food like this will help to cause spots, greasy skin and pounds of weight. It can even affect the appearance of your hair.

TREATS!

Have an occasional treat, but don't eat this kind of food every day. Think of all that pocket money you can save!

Stick to things like fruit if you want to eat in between meals or nibble on the bus home.

You'll soon notice how good your skin looks after you've switched to sensible food.

Eat plenty of fresh vegetables and salads. Also, lots of lean meat, preferably not fried! Get Mum to grill those steaks instead of frying them in lots of oil or butter!

It's a good idea to get Mum to join you in a healthy eating scheme. Bet she'll be delighted to help, as it'll improve her figure and skin too!

If your friends jeer at you for drinking pure orange juice instead of a Coke, just ignore them. They'll soon come round to your way of thinking when they see how your skin is gleaming! Also, water is good for you.

KEEPING FIT

Now you're eating all the right things, don't just sit back and think that's all there is to it! A bit of exercise wouldn't go amiss.

Alright, gym and PT at school may be boring or it may be fun, but there are other ways to keep yourself in trim and tone up those muscles. Go swimming, play squash or why not take up cycling?

Get a bunch of friends to go jogging with you after school a couple of evenings a week.

Buy yourself a bright 'n' cheeful tracksuit — you'll love running around to show it off!

EFFORT

If you want to be a real expert, your local library should have plenty of books on exercises. Get a couple out and have a look at them. Then choose the exercises you think you'll enjoy doing.

You could even invite a crowd of friends round one evening a week and exercise in time to your favourite music. That's good for a giggle!

Get Mum and Dad's permission first — especially as it'll probably mean Dad will have to move the furniture to make some floor space!

Put just a bit of effort into looking good by following these tips, and you'll soon be a Super Fit Miss!

The Trouble With Billy...

A Special Girl Story

'I had to keep my promise to my brother — he'd never forgive me otherwise!'

"Ugh!" Miss Patterson, my form mistress, said. "It's a rat!"

"It isn't," I said politely. "It's a gerbil."

"Well, it looks like a rat!" she shuddered. "It's horrible."

"He's not, really he's not. He's lovely!" I said. "His name's Billy Gerbil. D'you want to hold him?"

I dipped my hand into his cage and lifted him up! "He's lovely and soft and warm."

"Put him back at once!" Miss Patterson said. "I really don't think that I can allow that...that animal to stay in the school."

*   *   *

"Oh, please!" I said. "It's only for a term — while my brother goes abroad with Mum and Dad. There's no one else to have him."

She sighed and shook her head. "Well, I suppose if there's nowhere else he can go."

"Thanks, Miss Patterson! You won't regret it."

As a matter of fact, after three days she *did* regret it. Billy was a messy eater and Matron lost no time in complaining to her about a certain amount of sunflower seeds which he had scattered all over the dormitory floor.

"And I'm sure he smells," Matron said to me, turning up her nose.

"Oh, he doesn't!" I said heatedly. "Honestly he doesn't. Look, you can go right up to his cage and sniff. You won't smell a thing!"

"I'd rather not," Matron said. "And anyway, what about the mess he makes? Susan said she found a sunflower seed in her bed last night."

*   *   *

Susan would! I thought it, but didn't say anything. Susan had the bed next to mine, was a year older than me and was always trying to get me into trouble.

"I'll be more careful," I said to Matron. "I'll clean round his cage every day and you won't see another sunflower seed anywhere."

Matron looked down her nose disapprovingly. "Shouldn't be allowed," she said. "If there's any more trouble with him he'll have to go."

"But there's nowhere *for* him to go!"

"He can go to the pet shop in town. They can find him a proper home."

She left the dormitory, muttering. When she'd gone I turned to Billy.

"Don't you mind," I whispered. "I'll look after you. I won't let them take you away."

Billy looked at me and twitched his whiskers. He knew what I was trying to tell him; I was sure he did.

I just had to keep my promise to David my brother; he'd never forgive me otherwise.

For the next couple of days I was really careful. I cleaned out Billy's cage every morning, and I picked up every scrap of seed that fell out. Susan, of course, carried on examining her sheets every night.

Although she didn't find another sunflower seed between the sheets, she found something else to complain about. I woke up about twelve o'clock, one night, to hear her sighing loudly.

"What's up?" I asked, sitting up. "Are you ill?"

"It's that…that rat thing of yours! He's making such a terrible noise that I can't sleep!"

* * *

I held my breath and listened, but all I could hear was a little faint scratching sound as Billy crunched his seeds up. "You mean *that*?"

She nodded. "Can't you stop him?"

"But I can hardly hear a thing!"

"Then my ears must be a lot more sensitive than yours. You'll have to shut him up."

"How can I?" I said. "Gerbils sleep in the day and play at night. I can't change that."

"Then he'll have to go! I can't stand it another night. I'm going to speak to Matron in the morning!"

And with that, she pulled a pillow tightly over her head and turned her back on me.

"What can we do?" I whispered to Billy urgently. "She wants to get rid of you!"

Billy sat up in the moonlight, whiskers twitching. He seemed to be saying that he was sorry for all the trouble he was causing.

"I *know* that Matron will say you've got to go."

* * *

He scrabbled back in his feeding bowl again, sending sunflower seeds flying. "Hush!" I said, "Or she'll go to Matron now!"

I looked across at Susan fearfully but she didn't move; I think she was already asleep. She'd probably only stayed awake so she could make a fuss!

The next day, Miss Patterson sent for me and told me that I had to take Billy to the pet shop.

"I'm sorry you've got to let your brother down," she said. "But I've given it a try and it just hasn't worked, has it?"

"Please, Miss Patterson..."

She held up her hand. She had her cross face on. "No, it's no use pleading with me; I've made up my mind. That's enough, Sarah!"

I went straight up to tell Billy what had happened but he looked so snug and warm curled up tightly in the hay that I didn't have the heart to disturb him.

He'd find out soon enough what was happening, anyway. He'd realise I'd broken my promise when he was chucked in a big hutch with loads of other gerbils he'd never seen before.

* * *

At bedtime that night I turned my back very deliberately on Susan — but not before she'd had time to flash me one big, triumphant smile. It wasn't fair! I hated her! If only there was something I could do to get my own back on her.

While I was trying to think up something nasty I fell asleep, and when I woke up it was the middle of the night, with not a glimmer of light from the moon.

I realised at once who had woken me up — Billy. He was making a terrible noise this time; scritch-scratching, gnawing the bars and running round and round his cage like a mad thing.

"Quiet!" I hissed. "If Susan wakes up she'll have you out now! She'll march you straight down to Matron and create a lot of trouble!"

This time he didn't seem to understand what I said. It was almost as if he was trying to tell me something.

Suddenly I sat bolt upright in bed. I could smell something … hear something crackling … there was a fire somewhere!

* * *

With one leap I was out of bed, grabbing my dressing gown and Billy's cage.

"Fire!" I shouted, and I rushed to the other girls' beds and shook them awake. They ran to the other dorms and I raced down for Matron to ring the alarm bell and summon the fire brigade.

Within ten minutes — we all knew our fire drill — we were assembled in the yard outside and the fire engines had arrived to put out the fire which had started in the science lab. The damage wasn't too bad — but we all knew that it *could* have been if Billy hadn't woken me up.

Later — much later — some of us sat round drinking cocoa in Matron's room. We were all much too excited to sleep and, anyway, we all wanted to talk about Billy, hero of the night!

* * *

It wasn't talk about him going to the pet shop, either, it was talk about how clever and talented he was — in fact Miss Patterson said she'd like me to write to David to ask if we could keep Billy permanently. "He'd make a lovely school mascot," she said, looking at him fondly. "Don't you think so, Susan?"

"Oh yes! I've always loved gerbils!" Susan said, and she reached into Billy's cage and tickled him.

Well, Billy looked at me when she did that and, d'you know, I'm *sure* he winked...

ARE YOU LATE AGAIN?

Do you arrive everywhere with plenty of time to spare? Or are you always late for everything? Here's your chance to find out if you're a punctual puss or a late lazy-bones!

1. Rise and shine! It's time to get up and catch that bus to school. It goes past the end of your road at 8.15. Do you:

a) Get to the bus-stop with plenty of time to spare. You'd rather hang around than be late?

b) Catch the bus by the skin of your teeth — it's a real rush for you every morning?

c) Miss it most mornings — you just can't bear getting up?

2. Mum and Dad are going out for the evening. Mum's put a cake in the oven. It'll be ready by 7 o'clock. Do you:

a) Hover by the oven at least ten minutes before the cake should come out — you don't want to ruin Mum's hard work by bringing it out late?

b) Rush into the kitchen at ten minutes past seven — when you've suddenly remembered?

c) Forget all about it until you smell burning about 8 o'clock, when you're in the middle of watching your favourite TV programme?

3. You've agreed to go out with a friend for the afternoon and have told your folks you'll be back by 5 o'clock. Do you:

a) Get home by a quarter to five. You don't like getting home late because it's not fair to worry Mum and Dad?

b) Arrive home five minutes after five — phew — just in time?

c) Stroll in at 5.30. What difference does getting home half-an-hour late make?

4. Your best friend has agreed to come round and spend Saturday evening with you. She said she'd arrive at 6.30. By 7 o'clock she still hasn't turned up. Do you:

a) Frantically ring her wondering why she's late?

b) Give her another half-an-hour before phoning up to see where she's got to?

c) Don't worry about her — she'll turn up at some stage …?

5. You've got an appointment with the dentist at 4 o'clock. It's a date you're dreading. Do you:

a) Get there early, say by 3.30. Better to get it over and done with?

b) Arrive just on 4 o'clock. After all, you've got to face up to it?

c) Arrive late — perhaps the dentist won't see you after all …?

6. You are going out for the day with the family. Do you:

a) Get up an extra half-an-hour early so you can really spruce yourself up?

b) Get ready just in time — it's a bit of a scramble but you just make it?

c) Keep everyone waiting while you finish polishing your shoes?

SCORE

Mainly a's: You are never late for anything. In fact, you probably drive people mad by turning up early! Everyone can set their watches by you. Relax a little — the world isn't going to fall apart if you very occasionally turn up just five seconds late!

Mainly b's: Not bad! You could try harder but you generally just about make dates and get into school just on time. Don't slip up any more, otherwise you will start to arrive late for everything!

Mainly c's: Oh dear! You try, but you just can't get it together, can you? Come on, start looking at your watch — if you've got one — and pay attention to the time. Being late is being rude to others. Turn over a new leaf and surprise everyone by starting to turn up on time. If you haven't got a watch, ask for one for Christmas!

HOBBY SPOT SPECIAL

PLANTING SEEDS

Soak orange and lemon seeds overnight in water, then let them dry. Fill a yogurt pot with seed compost. Wet it, then plant the seeds 1.5cm deep. Cover the pot with pretty paper and leave in a warm, dark place for a few weeks. When shoots appear, put the pots in a sunny place.

MAKE A SIMPLE SKIRT

Use 2 squares of material 1½ times your hip measurement, plus a square 4'' × 4'' for a pocket. Sew sides together on the wrong side. Turn up 1 inch for the hem, then turn over 1 inch at the top. Hem ¼'' all round pocket on the wrong side and sew on to skirt. Thread elastic through hem at top to required width.

There, now you've got a smashing skirt all ready to wear! (Don't forget to pick some pretty material!)

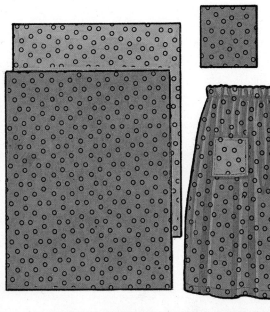

EASY CARDS AND CALENDARS

Cut pieces of white or coloured card to required size and fold in half. Decorate with lace or ribbon. You can either paint a pretty picture or make patterns with shapes of material. Try to make it as bright and interesting as possible.

For the calendar, mount your favourite picture onto a piece of coloured card and decorate in the same way as the cards. Add a matching coloured ribbon to the top and the calendar to the bottom. Easy, isn't it?

CANDLE DESIGNS

Decorate a large candle by arranging pressed flowers and fern on a paper pattern in the same design you want on the candle. Transfer pressed materials to candle by applying glue to the back of first the fern, then the flowers. Spray finished candle with clear Acrylic to protect candle and decorations. Now you've got a candle that's different!

DON'T GET CROSSWORD!

There's no need to get angry at this bumper crossword.
The answer's on Page 81.

What's Wrong With Rhona?

The girls of St. Bede's top hockey team were on a training run across Salisbury Plain. As usual, Rhona French was in the lead . . .

HEY, I CAN SMELL SCORCHING!

COME ON, YOU LOT, IT'S PROBABLY A SMALL BUSH FIRE!

PHEW! GOSH, RHONA, I'M GLAD YOU'RE IN OUR FORWARD LINE TOMORROW AND NOT — GASP — WITH THE OPPOSITION!

THANKS, HELEN. BUT I MUST PRACTISE SOME SHOOTING AT GOAL WHEN WE GET BACK!

SEE YOU LATER — I'M GOING TO SPRINT BACK TO SCHOOL.

YOU DO THAT. WE'RE HAVING A GENTLE JOG!

THAT SCORCHING SMELL'S QUITE STRONG HERE! HEY, LOOKS LIKE A DOLL OF SOME SORT LYING BY THE HEDGE.

FUNNY PLACE FOR A KID TO DROP IT. I'LL TAKE IT BACK TO SCHOOL AND SEE IF WE CAN FIND ITS OWNER.

WHAT HAVE YOU GOT THERE, RHONA?

JUST A DOLL I FOUND. IF I CAN'T TRACE THE OWNER, I'LL GIVE IT TO OUR JUMBLE SALE.

WELL, I WOULDN'T BUY IT. IT'S CREEPY. FEELS SORT OF SOFT, ALMOST LIKE REAL FLESH. BUT THE CLOTHES ARE PRETTY TRENDY.

YEAH. CAN'T BE MUCH GOOD — THE EYES DON'T EVEN OPEN. C'MON, LET'S GET CHANGED.

WHERE'S YOUR DOLL, RHONA?

BOTHER, I FORGOT IT! NEVER MIND, IT'LL BE SAFE IN MY LOCKER UNTIL THE MATCH TOMORROW.

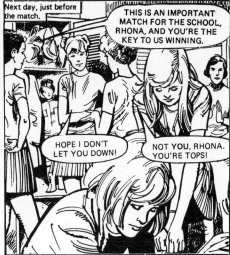

Next day, just before the match.

THIS IS AN IMPORTANT MATCH FOR THE SCHOOL, RHONA, AND YOU'RE THE KEY TO US WINNING.

HOPE I DON'T LET YOU DOWN!

NOT YOU, RHONA. YOU'RE TOPS!

TO YOU, RHONA – CENTRE!

GOT IT!

WHAT A MOVE – SHE SENT ME THE WRONG WAY!

GOAL! GREAT SHOT, RHONA!

At half-time. . .

I'D BETTER GO AND CHANGE MY STICK – THE BINDING'S COMING AWAY.

MIND YOU DON'T CHANGE YOUR **LUCK** WITH IT, EH?

BANG!

BOTHER, THE DOOR'S STUCK.

HEY, THE DOLL'S EYES HAVE OPENED. MY THUMPING ON THE LOCKER MUST HAVE DONE IT! OH WELL, CAN'T HANG ABOUT HERE ALL DAY!

OH HECK – I'VE SUDDENLY GOT A SPLITTING HEADACHE.

NOW EVERYTHING'S SPINNING – GOSH, I HOPE I'M NOT GOING TO PASS OUT!

HERE, RHONA, YOU'RE CLEAR. MAKE IT NUMBER TWO!

WH – WHAT THE – ? RHONA'S MISSED IT. SHE'S SUDDENLY PLAYING LIKE A NOVICE!

THEY'VE EQUALISED BECAUSE OF THAT MISTAKE! HEY, ARE YOU FEELING ALL RIGHT, RHONA?

M — MUMBLE.

QUICK, WE'RE UNMARKED. WHATEVER YOU DO, DON'T GIVE IT TO RHONA! SHE'S PLAYING THE FOOL FOR SOME REASON!

Rhona was a passenger for the rest of the game.

THEY'RE LEADING TWO-ONE NOW, AND THEY GOT BOTH THEIR GOALS BECAUSE OF RHONA! BEING THE STAR PLAYER SEEMS TO HAVE GONE TO HER HEAD!

St. Bede's lost 2-1.

RHONA, WHAT'S WRONG? YOU DON'T SEEM WELL.

GNUGH! MUMMBLE.

HA, HA. BUT FOR THEIR CAPTAIN MUCKING ABOUT, WE'D NEVER HAVE BEATEN THEM!

Stumbling back to her locker, Rhona never noticed the doll.

FLIP!

OH, MY HEAD —

LOOKS LIKE WE'VE LOST OUR CHANCE OF THE FINALS — THANKS TO YOU-KNOW-WHO! JUST WHAT'S WRONG WITH RHONA?

SHE'S GOT TOO BIG FOR HER BOOTS, THAT'S WHAT! LET'S SEND HER TO COVENTRY.

HEY, WHAT'S GOING ON? CHANGE BACK INTO YOUR GEAR — IT'S ONLY HALF-TIME!

SO YOU ARE SENDING US ALL UP! YOU LET US DOWN DELIBERATELY AND THINK IT'S A JOKE! WELL, WE'RE NOT LAUGHING!

THANKS TO YOU, THE SECOND-HALF WAS A FIASCO. YOU'VE MADE THE SCHOOL A LAUGHING STOCK! NOW GET OUT OF MY SIGHT. YOU MAKE ME SICK!

W — WHAT ARE YOU TALKING ABOUT? I — I CAN ONLY REMEMBER THE FIRST HALF . . .

D — DID I DO ALL THOSE DAFT THINGS THEY SAID? BUT MY MIND'S A BLANK — W — WHAT'S WRONG WITH ME?

IS SOMETHING WRONG, RHONA? YOU DON'T LOOK AT ALL WELL.

I – I DON'T KNOW, MUM. I HAD AN AWFUL HEADACHE AND FELT GIDDY . . . I MUST HAVE BLACKED OUT OR SOMETHING, 'COS THE GIRLS SAID I ACTED FUNNY, BUT I CAN'T REMEMBER A THING ABOUT IT.

IT . . . IT'S VERY WORRYING, THOUGH I DON'T SUPPOSE IT'S ANYTHING MUCH.

THERE'S NO SMOKE WITHOUT FIRE, DEAR. COME IN AND HAVE A NICE HOT CUP OF TEA –

– THEN YOU'D BETTER GO UP AND LIE DOWN FOR A WHILE, AND WE'LL SEE HOW YOU FEEL LATER.

NOT FEELING WELL, EH? THAT'S WHAT COMES OF DASHING ABOUT. PITY YOU DON'T SPEND MORE TIME ON YOUR STUDIES, AND LESS ON SPORT!

UGH. WHAT D'YOU BUY THIS FOR? IT GIVES ME A SORT O' CREEPY FEELING! CAN'T IMAGINE HOW EVEN A SOPPY GIRL COULD WANT SOMETHING THIS UGLY.

I FOUND IT ON THE PLAIN. IF I CAN'T TRACE THE OWNER, I'LL GIVE IT TO THE JUMBLE SALE. NOW, GIVE IT BACK, BEFORE YOU BREAK IT, TIM.

IF I'D REALLY ACTED THE WAY THE OTHERS SAID, *SURELY* I'D REMEMBER SOMETHING *ABOUT IT?* I REMEMBER GOING BACK TO MY LOCKER FOR ANOTHER HOCKEY STICK AND SEEING THE DOLL –

HELLO, THAT'S FUNNY, THE DOLL'S EYES HAVE OPENED AGAIN . . . IT SEEMS TO BE STARING AT ME! SUPPOSE I TOUCHED SOME SORT OF SPRING WHEN I PUT IT ON THE DRESSING-TABLE. OH WELL, I'D BETTER TRY AND GET SOME REST.

But a couple of minutes later, just as Rhona was dozing off . . .

ARRRGH, MY HEAD . . . IT'S SPLITTING AGAIN, JUST LIKE BEFORE. OH THIS IS HORRIBLE!

I – I MUST TRY TO KEEP CONTROL THIS TIME.

NO – NOT GOOD ENOUGH . . . CONCENTRATE!

THAT IS A LITTLE BETTER. AND SO IS THE VOICE – NOT JUST MUMBLES AS EARLIER.

YE-OUCH!

RHONA!

STILL GOT THAT SOPPY DOLL WITH YOU? HEY, WHAT'S WRONG, SIS. YOU SLEEP-WALKING OR SOMETHING?

THAT IS FOR YOUR RUDENESS — NASTY BOY!

WHAT WAS THAT FOR? IT REALLY HURT, YOU ROTTER!

I'M SURE YOUR SISTER DIDN'T MEAN IT. SHE'S NOT WELL!

I AM NOW QUITE WELL, AND I DID MEAN IT! THAT BOY . . .

HUSH, DEAR, LEAST SAID, SOONEST MENDED . . . HERE, IF YOU'RE SURE YOU'RE ALL RIGHT, WIPE UP WHILE I SCOUR THE SAUCEPANS.

VERY WELL.

OH NO, MY BEST SERVICE, TOO!

YOU SHOULD DRY THEM ONE AT A TIME. MORE HASTE, LESS SPEED, YOU KNOW!

THAT WAS CARELESS. I LET MY MIND WANDER.

A little later . . .

WHERE DO YOU WANT THESE PUT?

WHY, IN THE CUPBOARD OF COURSE! THAT'S WHERE THEY'RE ALWAYS KEPT.

I WISH RHONA WOULDN'T KEEP STARING AT ME, IT MAKES ME FEEL UNEASY! I THINK I'LL PUT THE RADIO ON, A LITTLE MUSIC MIGHT CHEER US BOTH UP.

RHONA – H – HOW DID YOU KNOW I WAS GOING TO PUT THE RADIO ON?

DID YOU NOT SAY . . . AH, NO, I UNDERSTAND!

29

I WISH RHONA WOULDN'T INSIST ON GOING TO SCHOOL TODAY . . . A FEW DAYS' REST WOULD DO HER GOOD.

YOU'VE BEEN WAITING ON HER HAND AND FOOT . . . A GOOD HIDING WOULD HAVE BROUGHT HER TO HER SENSES QUICKER, IN MY OPINION.

SURELY THE GIRLS WILL REALISE IT WASN'T MY FAULT . . . HEY! THAT DOLL I FOUND — ITS EYES HAVE SOMEHOW **OPENED** AGAIN!

OH WELL, NO TIME TO TRY TO FIND OUT HOW THEY WORK NOW . . . I'VE GOT A COUPLE OF MINUTES TO FINISH GETTING READY.

OH NO! MY HEAD IS BEGINNING TO ACHE AGAIN, BUT . . . BUT IT'S NOT AS BAD AS BEFORE . . .

CRIKEY! I — I'M BEGINNING TO SEE THINGS, TOO . . . I'D BETTER SIT DOWN A MINUTE.

THAT IS BETTER. NOW FOR THIS SCHOOL.

HOW DO I GET THERE?

GOODBYE, DEAR. HAVE A NICE . . .

THOSE GIRLS ARE WEARING THE SAME JACKET AS I. I WILL JOIN THEM.

RHONA — LOOK OUT! GET BACK!

ARRRRGH!

SHE . . . SHE SEEMED TO TRIP – THE POOR BLOKE DIDN'T STAND A CHANCE! OH GOLLY, SHE'S LAYING AWFULLY STILL!

SEND AN AMBULANCE TO CASTLE STREET, FAST! ACCIDENT INVOLVING SCHOOLGIRL PEDESTRIAN AND MOTOR VEHICLE.

LET ME THROUGH – I'M A DOCTOR.

SHE STEPPED RIGHT OUT IN FRONT OF ME! I SWERVED – BUT SHE SOMEHOW TRIPPED.

THAT'S RIGHT! IT WAS ALMOST LIKE SHE LOST CONTROL OF HER LEGS!

Soon –

ONLY MINOR INJURIES, BUT I'VE GIVEN HER A STRONG SEDATIVE TO HELP HER SLEEP, AND MINIMISE SHOCK. LET ME KNOW WHEN SHE WAKES.

VERY WELL, DOCTOR.

WHAT HAS HAPPENED? WHERE AM I?

HUSH NOW, DEAR. YOU'RE IN HOSPITAL. YOU HAD AN ACCIDENT, BUT YOU'RE QUITE SAFE NOW.

THEN WHY AM I IN SUCH PAIN? SOB.

THE DOCTOR WILL SOON GIVE YOU SOMETHING FOR THAT.

HELLO, YOUNG LADY. HOW ARE YOU NOW? IT'S AFTER SEVEN, AND YOU'VE NEARLY SLEPT THE CLOCK ROUND.

OH NO!

I MUST GET HOME AT ONCE!

CALM YOURSELF, MY DEAR! IF IT'S YOUR PARENTS YOU'RE WORRIED ABOUT, THEY KNOW ALL ABOUT IT. THEY EVEN LOOKED IN TO SEE YOU! ALL BEING WELL, THEY CAN TAKE YOU HOME TOMORROW.

TOMORROW WILL BE TOO LATE – YOU DON'T UNDERSTAND!

SHE'S HYSTERICAL – MUST BE DELAYED SHOCK. PREPARE ANOTHER SEDATIVE.

I'LL BRING YOU SOMETHING TO MAKE YOU FEEL BETTER.

NOW'S MY CHANCE!

COME BACK, RHONA!

LEAVE ME ALONE, YOU STUPID WOMAN!

DON'T BE SILLY — YOU'RE NOT WELL ENOUGH TO — AGH!

THAT WILL SLOW HER DOWN.

SOMEONE STOP HER!

I MUST GET HOME, THERE IS LITTLE TIME! BUT WHICH WAY IS HOME!

IT IS HELEN! THIS IS FORTUNATE — SHE CAN TAKE ME HOME!

TAKE ME HOME AT ONCE.

HEY, YOU SHOULDN'T BE RUNNING AROUND LIKE THAT — I HEARD ABOUT YOUR ACCIDENT.

NEVER MIND THAT, I MUST GET BACK HOME AT ONCE!

OKAY, COME ON THEN . . . I GUESS IT WOULD BE BETTER IF YOUR PARENTS DEALT WITH THIS ANYWAY.

THERE SHE IS! GET HER IN THE CAR — WE MUST TAKE HER BACK TO THE HOSPITAL.

OH NO!

KEEP AWAY! OH YOU FOOLS . . . IF I DON'T GET HOME WITHIN THE HOUR, BOTH OF US WILL DIE!

BOTH? POOR GIRL'S IN SHOCK, BUT THE INJECTION WILL SOON CALM HER DOWN. BACK TO THE HOSPITAL NOW!

NO! Y – YOU MUST LET ME GO – OR WE'LL BOTH DIE!

I CAN'T LIVE I TELL YOU . . . I MUST HAVE THE DOLL . . . THE DOLL . . .

POOR KID. BUT A FEW DAYS REST SHOULD MAKE HER BETTER.

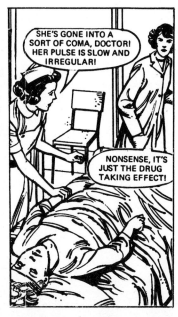

SHE'S GONE INTO A SORT OF COMA, DOCTOR! HER PULSE IS SLOW AND IRREGULAR!

NONSENSE, IT'S JUST THE DRUG TAKING EFFECT!

YOU'RE RIGHT! HEAVENS – I CAN'T UNDERSTAND IT. GET HER TO INTENSIVE CARE IMMEDIATELY!

YES, DOCTOR!

SEE HER PARENTS ARE NOTIFIED AT ONCE!

A little later –

WHERE'S RHONA? WE MUST SEE HER!

I – IS SHE CONSCIOUS?

YOU CAN'T GO IN JUST NOW, MRS. FRENCH. THEY'RE DOING EVERYTHING THEY CAN FOR HER!

NOT COMPLETELY . . . BUT SHE KEEPS MUTTERING SOMETHING ABOUT A DOLL – WOULD THAT MEAN ANYTHING TO YOU?

MUST BE THAT WEIRD LOOKING DOLL SHE FOUND – LORD KNOWS WHY – IT'S HORRIBLE! STILL, I'LL NIP BACK FOR IT.

RESPIRATION 30 AND SHALLOW.

BLOOD PRESSURE 40 OVER ZERO.

34

WE . . . WE'VE LOST HER, DOCTOR!

OUT OF MY WAY — IF MY DAUGHTER WANTS THIS DOLL, SHE'S GOING TO HAVE IT!

I — I'M AFRAID YOU'RE TOO LATE, MR. FRENCH!

W — WHAT — RHONA'S —

CLICK!

M — MY HEAD'S SWIMMING AND . . . GOSH! IT . . . IT'S ALL BANDAGED —

IT — IT'S A MIRACLE!

RHONA!

HELLO, DAD! WHAT AM I DOING HERE? WHAT . . . WHAT'S HAPPENED TO ME? ALL I CAN REMEMBER IS GETTING READY FOR SCHOOL.

HER HEART AND BREATHING ARE NORMAL AGAIN!

Next day, Rhona had a visitor — Helen.

REMEMBER THAT DOLL YOU FOUND ON SALISBURY PLAIN? BRENDA WAS TELLING ME HER KID SISTER LOST A DOLL SOMEWHERE ROUND THERE — MUST HAVE FALLEN OUT OF HER PUSH-CHAIR.

I'LL TAKE IT TO SCHOOL FOR BRENDA TO TAKE A LOOK AT, AS SOON AS THEY LET ME OUT OF HERE.

THAT COULD BE TOMORROW, KIDDO. DOC'S PLEASED WITH YOU NOW. REAL HANDFUL WHEN YOU CAME IN, THOUGH!

S — SORRY, NURSE. BUT I JUST DON'T REMEMBER A THING ABOUT IT. HONEST.

A few days later, Rhona was ready for school again!

ARE YOU SURE YOU'RE ALL RIGHT, DEAR? NO SENSE PUSHING THINGS!

I'M FINE, MUM. CHEERIO, TIM!

TIM AND THE OTHERS WERE RIGHT. THIS DOLL IS SORT OF CREEPY. I SHAN'T BE SORRY TO GET SHOT OF IT!

HI, RHONA – GOOD TO SEE YOU BACK! SORRY WE COLD-SHOULDERED YOU AFTER THE HOCKEY MATCH – WE DIDN'T KNOW YOU WERE ILL.

THANKS, GANG. GOOD TO BE BACK!

ANYTHING MUCH HAPPENED WHILE I'VE BEEN AWAY, BETTE?

SHUSH, HERE'S MISS FAVERSHAM.

GET OUT YOUR MATHS BOOKS. WE'LL START WITH SOME PROBLEMS INVOLVING DIFFERENTIAL EQUATIONS, AND SEE HOW MUCH YOU REMEMBER FROM YESTERDAY'S LESSON.

GROAN.

THE DOLL – AND ITS EYES ARE OPEN AGAIN!

OH NO! MY HEAD... IT'S THROBBING AGAIN – LIKE THE OTHER DAY!

AND... AND I'M SEEING STRANGE PICTURES AGAIN. OH HECK, WHAT IS GOING TO HAPPEN TO ME THIS TIME?

STOP DAY-DREAMING, RHONA, AND OPEN YOUR BOOK. AS YOU WEREN'T HERE YESTERDAY, I'LL TRY TO EXPLAIN HOW WE TACKLE THIS SORT OF PROBLEM.

HUH? OH, VERY WELL.

HA, HA! THERE IS CERTAINLY NO NEED TO EXPLAIN SUCH A SIMPLE PIECE OF ELEMENTARY ARITHMETIC TO ME!

DON'T BE CHILDISH, RHONA!

IT IS THIS THAT IS CHILDISH – SURELY YOU ARE CAPABLE OF TEACHING TO A HIGHER STANDARD THAN THAT!

RHONA MUST HAVE FLIPPED RAGGING MISS FAVERSHAM LIKE THAT! SHE'S A GOOD SORT, BUT I CAN'T SEE HER STANDING FOR IT!

I KNOW YOU'VE BEEN ILL, BUT THAT'S NO EXCUSE FOR...

TAKE YOUR HAND OFF ME, AT ONCE. HOW DARE YOU TOUCH ME, YOU HORRID WOMAN!

I'VE NEVER HEARD SUCH INSOLENCE! WE'LL SEE WHAT THE HEAD HAS TO SAY ABOUT THIS!

CRIKEY, SHE'S LIKE JEKYLL AND HYDE – ALL RIGHT ONE MINUTE AND A MONSTER THE NEXT. THERE'S SOMETHING WRONG WITH RHONA – BUT WHAT?

YOUR BEHAVIOUR TOWARDS MISS FAVERSHAM IS UNPARDONABLE, RHONA! I WILL NOT TOLERATE SUCH CONDUCT IN MY SCHOOL!

I MERELY PUSHED HER ASIDE. IT WAS HER FAULT FOR LAYING HER HAND ON ME!

UNDER THE CIRCUMSTANCES, PERHAPS SENDING THE GIRL HOME WITH A STRONG LETTER TO HER PARENTS WILL BE SUFFICIENT...

COLLECT YOUR THINGS AND GO, RHONA!

Rhona returned to her classroom...

I CAN ONLY SUPPOSE YOU WERE PLAYING SOME STUPID JOKE, RHONA. WELL, I'M SURE YOU'RE SORRY NOW.

IT WAS NOT A JOKE — AND I AM NOT SORRY!

BLESS MY SOUL, WHAT HAS COME OVER THE CHILD?

POOR RHONA. SOMETHING'S HAPPENED TO HER AGAIN...I'LL CALL ROUND AND SEE HER THIS EVENING. SHE NEVER USED TO BE IN TROUBLE AT ALL, BUT JUST LATELY — WELL!

I KNOW THE WAY HOME, NOW. I'LL LOOK AROUND THE TOWN FOR A WHILE.

FRESH UP FROM THE COUNTRY TODAY, LADY.

THIS IS INTERESTING.

HOW QUAINT TO TRADE IN THE OPEN LIKE THAT.

BLIMEY, I WISH THAT GIRL WOULD STOP STARING AT ME LIKE THAT...HER EYES FAIR GIVE ME THE CREEPS!

LOOK, KID, IF YOU DON'T WANT TO BUY NOTHING — HOP IT!

Rhona sent the apples flying...

HEY, WHAT THE –?

LITTLE HOOLIGAN..!

HOW DARE HE ADDRESS ME LIKE THAT!

Later that evening, Helen came round to see Rhona as she'd promised —

HEY, ARE YOU ALL RIGHT, RHONA? YOU LOOK PRETTY PALE!

DAD'S BEEN ON AT ME AGAIN. SEEMS I'M SUPPOSED TO HAVE DELIBERATELY KNOCKED OVER A LOAD OF APPLES IN THE MARKET.

YOU? HECK, YOU'D NEVER DO ANYTHING LIKE THAT!

B-BUT I'M SUPPOSED TO HAVE DONE SO MANY STRANGE THINGS LATELY AND I CAN'T REMEMBER THEM! OH, HELEN, WHAT IS WRONG WITH ME?

THE DOCTORS CAN'T FIND ANYTHING WRONG. LET'S SEE IF WE CAN FIND A LINK.

IT ALL STARTED AT THAT HOCKEY MATCH.

OH YES, THAT'S RIGHT. AND ON THE DAY BEFORE, WE HAD A RUN AND YOU FOUND THAT WEIRD DOLL ON THE PLAIN.

THAT DOLL!

NO, THAT'S STUPID! HOW COULD A DOLL HAVE ANYTHING TO DO WITH IT?

SEARCH ME, BUT THE THING DOES GIVE ME THE CREEPS!

IT MIGHT SOUND SILLY, BUT WHY NOT GET RID OF IT JUST IN CASE? BETTER SAFE THAN SORRY, AS YOUR MUM WOULD SAY.

CAN'T DO ANY HARM...COME ON, IT'S UP IN MY ROOM!

But after a search —

IT'S FUNNY. I CAN'T FIND IT ANYWHERE!

YOU HAD IT WITH YOU WHEN YOU STALKED OUT OF THE CLASSROOM.

BET YOU DROPPED IT SOMEWHERE — OR PUT IT DOWN AND FORGOT IT.

THAT MUST BE IT.

ANYWAY, IT'S GONE NOW, AND GOOD RIDDANCE!

SO ANYTHING THAT HAPPENS NOW, CAN'T BE BECAUSE OF THE DOLL, RIGHT?

Next morning —

I HOPE DAD WASN'T TOO HARD ON YOU, DEAR. HIS BARK'S WORSE THAN HIS BITE!

YOU COULD HAVE FOOLED ME, MUM! BUT NO, HE'S ALL RIGHT — REALLY STUCK UP FOR ME WHEN I WAS RIGHT IN THE CART — AND IF I DID DO THOSE THINGS, I ASKED FOR IT!

HI, RHONA. ER, HOW YOU FEELING TODAY?

FINE. I DON'T KNOW IF IT'S BEING RID OF THAT DOLL OR NOT, BUT I'VE A FEELING EVERYTHING'S GOING TO BE OKAY NOW!

But in the class —

HI, SHEILA... HEY! WHAT'S THE MATTER?

HUH! WHAT'S THE MATTER, SHE ASKS... AFTER ACTING LIKE SHE OWNS THE SCHOOL!

LOOK, I'M SORRY. I DIDN'T KNOW WHAT I WAS DOING!

HEY, IT'S THE SCHOOL CAPTAIN! WONDER WHAT SHE WANTS.

WE'VE THREE MEMBERS OF THE FIRST HOCKEY SIDE DOWN WITH 'FLU. IT GOES AGAINST THE GRAIN, BUT I'M PUTTING YOU BACK IN THE TEAM FOR SATURDAY'S MATCH.

GOSH, THANKS. I WON'T LET YOU DOWN AGAIN!

GROAN. WE'VE LOST FOR SURE NOW!

BET SHE'LL PLAY THE GOAT LIKE SHE DID LAST TIME!

NO. I'M NOT GOING TO HAVE THESE BLACKOUTS ANYMORE — I FEEL FINE. B-BUT JUST SUPPOSING...?

On Saturday. . .

I—I HOPE I DON'T MAKE A FOOL OF MYSELF THIS TIME, HELEN.

OF COURSE YOU WON'T, RHONA. GET IT INTO YOUR HEAD—NOW THAT DOLL'S GONE, YOU'RE BACK TO BEING YOUR REAL SELF!

FANCY GIVING THAT KID ANOTHER CHANCE! BOO!

BETTER IF WE'D PLAYED ONE GIRL SHORT.

I'LL SHOW THEM. . . OH, I—I HOPE I CAN!

The game had barely started when—

TO ME, JUDY—I'M UNMARKED!

IT'S AGAINST MY BETTER JUDGEMENT TO PASS TO HER, BUT HERE GOES—

IT'S AN OPEN GOAL. OH PLEASE DON'T LET ME MISS!

OH NO, THE WHISTLE. I WAS OFF-SIDE—I'VE LET THE TEAM DOWN AGAIN!

HARD LUCK, RHONA!

THANKS, BUT I WAS OFF-SIDE. . .I'LL MAKE SURE I'M NOT NEXT TIME!

Just before half-time—

RHONA—TO YOU!

THIS IS MY CHANCE TO MAKE IT UP WITH THE GIRLS. I MUSTN'T MUCK IT UP THIS TIME!

Continued On P.82

STING

A Girl Pin-Up

Way back in 1976, Sting and his wife, Frances, decided that he would leave his safe job as a teacher in Newcastle and head for London town.

So Sting handed in his notice, loaded all his possessions into their battered old car and made for London.

"Everybody told me I was crazy," said Sting. "But I know I had to make the break or I would have gone mad!" It certainly paid off, 'cos Sting's never looked back since.

Winter, Spring, You Can Still

Make the most of yourself all year round...

You know what it's like when you've got a streaming cold. Your eyes are puffy and swollen, your nose is red and your mouth is sore. Not a pretty sight, huh? But you're fed up with staying indoors and it's your best friend's party. You don't want to miss it, so what do you do?

First of all, put lots of moisturiser on your face. Something like Nivea cream or baby lotion will do the trick. If you've got a very red face, see if Mum's got some green powder or cream. This is a good trick to tone down your colour. Also very good if you blush!

WATERPROOF!

Make sure that you use a waterproof mascara. You don't want black lines running down your face, do you?

Finish off with masses of lipgloss. As well as giving them a shine, it'll help your lips heal.

All you need do now is massage some dry shampoo into your hair. Leave it for a few minutes, then brush it out thoroughly.

Now you're all set to go. Make sure you take plenty of tissues with you and you probably won't even need them! What's more, nobody will even know you've got a cold!

PLAN AHEAD

When you see the first hint of spring sunshine, don't be fooled! It doesn't mean that summer has come, so don't go rushing into your light summery clothes.

Sit down and sort out your summer wardrobe. Be ruthless and throw out anything you're not likely to wear.

Now is the time to start planning those long, hot days ahead. If you want to lose weight before you slip on a bikini, cut out cakes, sweets, chocolate, potatoes and sugar.

If you want to add weight, make sure you sit down and eat three proper square meals. Leave off the junk food because it'll only make you feel slow and lazy!

HEALTHY

Summer is the time to let your skin breathe. Don't wear any face make-up so the sun can

GIRL BEAUTY GUIDE

Summer, Autumn Look Good!

get to your skin. You'll feel really good once you've got a light tan and you'll look so healthy and attractive!

Eat lots of salads, vegetables and fresh fruit and your figure will look after itself. It's a great time for taking lots of exercise — swimming, tennis, jogging, cycling and walking! Make sure that you get out as much as possible and breathe in the fresh air.

Be careful to check your personal freshness. If you need to, use a deodorant or antiperspirant to stop any body odour. And if you have body hair under your arms and down your legs, you may wish to gently shave it off

before you pop on your new bikini.

EASY STYLE

Choose an easy hairstyle for the summer. You want to be able to give it a quick shampoo then let it dry naturally.

If possible, try not to wear the same pair of shoes or sandals two days running. Give them a rest! Also, if you're going shopping, make sure that you're wearing comfortable shoes.

Treat yourself to a manicure and pedicure once a month when you get the bathroom to yourself. (Check that nobody else wants to use it first!)

Always wear a fresh pair of knickers, socks and a vest or bra every day. Try and get into the habit of rinsing them through every night — it'll only take a few minutes and it means you'll always have clean undies. Also, it'll help Mum out too!

If you can't have a bath or shower every day, at least have an all-over wash. Match up soap, talc and eau de cologne so you smell as fresh as a daisy!

FADING...

September sees the start of the school year and autumn!

Your tan will start to fade and so will your holiday memories. It's back to uniforms, homework, exams and early nights!

It's very important that you get plenty of sleep. Don't put off doing your homework until the last minute because you don't want to be up half the night, do you?

GOOD FOOD!

Another good tip is to drink lots of water. It'll make your eyes sparkle and it's so good for your skin and insides.

Don't be tempted to skip school dinners and fill up with stodge. Try to have a proper lunch. You can always finish off with fruit or a yogurt — much better for you than crisps and pastries!

Follow this guide, keep reading our *Girl* beauty pages and you can't go wrong!

YOUR ★ LUC

ARIES
Mar 21 – Apr 20

You're one of those strong people who everyone likes to have around to take charge of things. Once you get an idea in your head, you like to see it through. You enjoy travel and are lucky with your health. Lucky colours: All shades of red.

TAURUS
Apr 21 – May 21

The mad bull in you only comes out when you are upset. The rest of the time you are patient, reliable and honest. You're good with money — in fact, so good, your friends might think you're being mean — not just careful. Lucky colour: Blue.

LEO
Jul 24 – Aug 23

You're smashing to have as a friend and you're a very good listener. You'll probably find friends come to you with their troubles, but you find it hard to share yours. You have a very forgiving nature, but you might get very depressed if a friend lets you down badly. Lucky colours: Yellow and gold.

VIRGO
Aug 24 – Sep 23

You plod along at your own pace quite happily, regardless of what's going on around you. You worry too much sometimes, especially about your weight and general health. But because you have good money sense, you make marvellous chemists, or models! Lucky colours: Brown and grey.

SAGITTARIUS
Nov 23 – Dec 21

What a lucky girl! You always look on the bright side, even when things aren't going as well as they might. Of course, you have your faults, like the rest of us — untidiness is one of your worst! But, generally, you're fun to be with. Lucky colours: Purple and maroon.

CAPRICORN
Dec 22 – Jan 20

You drive friends mad because you'll never be hurried into doing anything. You always take your time to come to the right decision because that's your nature. You mind your own business and don't listen to gossip about people. Lucky colours: Black and dark brown.

KY ☆ STARS

GEMINI
May22-Jun21

You're a bit of a clever-clogs really, aren't you? You just love anything new and you believe in the old saying 'actions speak louder than words.' You love children and animals and you're a kind, loyal friend. Lucky colours: Yellow, orange and green.

CANCER
Jun22-Jul23

You are emotional, sensitive, imaginative and romantic. You like to be noticed and you usually get your own way. You have a good memory, but it can be dangerous to upset you as you can turn nasty. Mostly though, you are kind-hearted. Lucky colours: Green and grey.

LIBRA
Sep24-Oct23

You are not easily fooled and the one thing you can never forgive is someone who lies to you. You can always see both sides of an argument, which can mean you're often torn between people you love. Lucky colours: Green, blue and brown.

SCORPIO
Oct24-Nov22

There's nothing you like more than being praised and encouraged when you do something well, but don't get bad-tempered if it doesn't happen. You have a jealous streak which can be dangerous, but usually you manage to control it. Lucky colours: Dark red and crimson.

AQUARIUS
Jan21-Feb19

You're what most people would call 'the quiet type.' You think a lot and you have a deep understanding of other people and sympathy for their troubles. You tend to be a little selfish and, if you're not careful, you could get a big head because you tend to do well in everything you attempt. Lucky colours: Blacks or blues.

PISCES
Feb20 Mar20

The trouble with you is that you're so easily led! You go along with the crowd because it's the easiest thing to do, but it's often not what you really want. You get easily bored and depressed — but when you're happy, you're on top of the world. Lucky colours: Blue

BRIAN ALDRED

MAKE IT UP!

YOU CAN DO IT...

Have lots of fun on a wet afternoon making these fun things. They're great for unusual present ideas, so why not make an extra set?

ROB. Kightley ©

RAG MAN

Ever wondered how to use up all those scraps of material left after dressmaking? Well, here's an easy way to turn them into a colourful rag-doll you can hang up in your bedroom.

First, cut out lots of circles about 9cm radius from your material scraps. Once you have cut one, you can use it as a pattern for the others. Now using large stitches, sew around the circles of material about 5mms in from the edge. These stitches are then used to gather in the material as shown in the illustration. Secure the cotton.

Body

Once you have done a few, just thread them onto some strong cotton using the needle. Thread quite a few for the body, and make two separate ones for the arms. These can be sewn on the body.

To finish off your man, use a strong glue to stick on a ping-pong ball for a head. Now you will have to paint on a face! Using some large beads, sew them on for the feet and hands.

And there you have him, your own rag man!

PAPER MACHE BEADS

Here's an interesting way to make your own beads.

Cut long strips of white paper, cover them in wallpaper paste, then wrap around a knitting needle as shown in the illustration.

You can use different lengths and widths of paper, to make various sized beads.

Once completely dry, take them off the knitting needle and paint a pretty colour. Patterned ones look very attractive, and a coat of varnish will protect them. Now either thread them onto cotton to make a lovely necklace and bracelet, or another idea is to attach some coloured cord to a brass curtain ring. This makes a very unusual pendant or key ring.

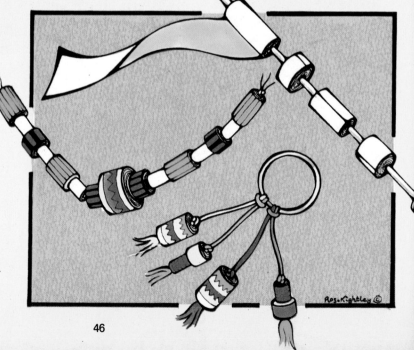

RogerKightley ©

Girl

GROWING OLD

You'd never think, to look at me,
An elderly, dignified ram.
That I was once a fluffy, young,
Loveable little lamb.

But like all things, one ages.
And days slip by, one fears.
So make the most of your childhood
And those passing years.

JANUARY					
Monday		4	11	18	25
Tuesday		5	12	19	26
Wednesday	3	13	20	27	
Thursday		7	14	21	28
Friday	1	8	15	22	29
Saturday	2	9	16	23	30
Sunday	3	10	17	24	31

FEBRUARY				
Monday	1	8	15	22
Tuesday	2	9	16	23
Wednesday	3	10	17	24
Thursday	4	11	18	25
Friday	5	12	19	26
Saturday	6	13	20	27
Sunday	7	14	21	28

MARCH					
Monday	1	8	15	22	29
Tuesday	2	9	16	23	30
Wednesday	3	10	17	24	31
Thursday	4	11	18	25	
Friday	5	12	19	26	
Saturday	6	13	20	27	
Sunday	7	14	21	28	

Girl

SWIMMING

The water looks inviting.
Should I chance a swim?
Or wait until the sun is hot
Before I tumble in?

The water may be warm enough,
But one thought does occur:
'Do I really want to hang about
In a coat of soaking fur?'

APRIL					
Monday		5	12	19	26
Tuesday		6	13	20	27
Wednesday		7	14	21	28
Thursday	1	8	15	22	29
Friday	2	9	16	23	30
Saturday	3	10	17	24	
Sunday	4	11	18	25	

MAY					
Monday		3	10	17	24	31
Tuesday		4	11	18	25	
Wednesday		5	12	19	26	
Thursday		6	13	20	27	
Friday		7	14	21	28	
Saturday	1	8	15	22	29	
Sunday	2	9	16	23	30	

JUNE					
Monday		7	14	21	28
Tuesday	1	8	15	22	29
Wednesday	2	9	16	23	30
Thursday	3	10	17	24	
Friday	4	11	18	25	
Saturday	5	12	19	26	
Sunday	6	13	20	27	

Girl

LOST

I'm sure I had it this morning,
It was here a moment ago.
But it seems I must have dropped it.
I've searched both high and low.

Can you give me some assistance?
I'm really quite fond of the thing.
So do look carefully, my dears
And find my left earring.

JULY					
Monday		5	12	19	26
Tuesday		6	13	20	27
Wednesday		7	14	21	28
Thursday	1	8	15	22	29
Friday	2	9	16	23	30
Saturday	3	10	17	24	31
Sunday	4	11	18	25	

AUGUST					
Monday		2	9	16	23	30
Tuesday		3	10	17	24	31
Wednesday		4	11	18	25	
Thursday		5	12	19	26	
Friday		6	13	20	27	
Saturday		7	14	21	28	
Sunday	1	8	15	22	29	

SEPTEMBER					
Monday		6	13	20	27
Tuesday		7	14	21	28
Wednesday	1	8	15	22	29
Thursday	2	9	16	23	30
Friday	3	10	17	24	
Saturday	4	11	18	25	
Sunday	5	12	19	26	

Girl

CHRISTMAS TIME

Come Christmas time and jingle bells
And snow and holly and a paper hat
And Santa Claus and mistletoe
And me, a gift-wrapped cat!

OCTOBER					
Monday		4	11	18	25
Tuesday		5	12	19	26
Wednesday		6	13	20	27
Thursday		7	14	21	28
Friday	1	8	15	22	29
Saturday	2	9	16	23	30
Sunday	3	10	17	24	31

NOVEMBER					
Monday	1	8	15	22	29
Tuesday	2	9	16	23	30
Wednesday	3	10	17	24	
Thursday	4	11	18	25	
Friday	5	12	19	26	
Saturday	6	13	20	27	
Sunday	7	14	21	28	

DECEMBER					
Monday		6	13	20	27
Tuesday		7	14	21	28
Wednesday	1	8	15	22	29
Thursday	2	9	16	23	30
Friday	3	10	17	24	31
Saturday	4	11	18	25	
Sunday	5	12	19	26	

Are You a Perfect Pupil?

Whether you like it or not, you've got to go to school! Find out here if you're the perfect pupil or think school's one big bore ...

1. Your teacher certainly believes in giving you plenty of home-work! Do you:
a) Go home and do it straight away so you can relax in peace for the rest of the evening?
b) Leave it to the last minute just before you're due to go to bed?
c) Copy your best friend's on the bus the next morning?

2. A test's coming up soon. Ugh! Do you:
a) Swot up on the subject the night before for hours on end — you want top marks?
b) Have a quick look at your books half-an-hour beforehand. That's what revision means, doesn't it?
c) Don't bother — you've got plenty of other better things to do than revise for tests?

3. Your head-teacher's dead strict about arriving on time for school. Do you:
a) Always arrive on time — in fact, you generally get there with bags of time to spare?
b) Rush into school right on the dot every morning?
c) Arrive late most mornings and land yourself in deep water?

4. Your teacher suddenly announces that your school is going out to visit a local museum one afternoon. Do you:
a) Think it's a great idea. You can't wait to go?
b) Agree to go along though you're not exactly keen — but it does mean an afternoon out of the classroom?
c) Think the idea is dreadful! You make sure you're off 'sick' that day so you don't have to go?

5. Your school has lots of activities after school like a drama club and a sports club. Do you:
a) Join all of them — you might as well get as much as you can out of school and make lots of friends?
b) Join one and go along every so often when you feel like it?
c) Don't bother with any of them. It's straight home to watch TV every night for you?

6. There's a subject you just loathe at school. You are useless at it. Do you:
a) Have a real good 'go' at overcoming it — after all, practice makes perfect?
b) Go along, but sit at the back of the class so the teacher won't pick on you and ask questions you know you can't answer?
c) Disappear into the sick room with a 'raging headache' when the subject comes round on your school time-table?

MAINLY a's: There's no doubt about it — you are the perfect pupil! Chances are you are head girl, a prefect or near the top of your class. Try not to take school too seriously — have some fun sometimes!

MAINLY b's: You are like most pupils — sometimes good, sometimes bad! Make a real effort to work harder at the subjects you're not very good at — you'll enjoy school all the more once you've improved on them and understand things better.

MAINLY c's: Heading for the bottom of the class, that's you! Pull your socks up and settle down to some work. There are some rewards in working hard and it doesn't take that much effort!

If the best you can manage is baked beans on toast, take over the kitchen for an afternoon and try these scrummy recipes. They're all easy to follow and they taste absolutely delicious!

BACON AND EGG SUPPER

You need:
2oz/50g back bacon
2 eggs, beaten
salt and pepper
Worcestershire sauce
1 slice bread

Reserve two small rashers of bacon and chop the rest. In a small pan, fry the bacon rashers and pieces until crisp. Remove the rashers and keep warm. Pour in the egg and add seasoning and Worcestershire sauce to taste. Stir continuously until scrambled.

Meanwhile, toast the bread, top with reserved rashers and pile on the scrambled egg mixture.

CURRY SAUSAGES WITH RICE

You need:
1lb/500g pork sausages
pinch of salt
2 teaspoons/2 × 5ml spoon curry powder
2 teaspoons/2 × 5ml spoon coriander powder
¼ teaspoon/¼ × 5ml spoon chilli powder
6oz/150g long grain rice
2 teaspoons/2 × 5ml spoon tumeric
salt and pepper
1 teaspoon/1 × 5ml spoon chopped parsley
watercress to garnish

Mix the salt, curry powder, coriander and chilli together. Rub the mixture lightly over the sausages. Grill in the grill pan with the rack removed, for 15 minutes, turning frequently.

Cook the rice in boiling salted water with the tumeric for about 12 minutes. Once cooked, drain, season well and mix with chopped parsley.

Serve the sausages on the rice, with a salad.

SPICY MEXICAN STEW

You need:
1 onion, chopped
oil for frying
12oz (300g) minced beef
1oz (25g) flour
2-3 tbsp (2-3 × 15ml) Kraft Mexican Relish
1 × 14oz (400g) can baked beans
½pt (250ml) beef stock

Fry the onion gently in the oil until soft. Add the meat and cook briskly, stirring, until well browned.

Stir in the flour, then add the relish, beans and stock.

Cover and simmer very gently for 30-40 minutes. Great for a cold, wintery day!

SALMON AND CORN CAKES

You need:
1½lb potatoes — peeled and diced
salt and pepper
1oz butter
8oz can flaked salmon
7oz can Green Giant Niblets Corn, drained
1 large egg, beaten
golden crumbs for coating
oil for frying

Sauce:
1 large onion, finely chopped
1 tablespoon corn oil
14½oz can tomatoes — sieved
1 tablespoon tomato puree
1 chicken stock cube

Cook the potatoes in boiling salted water until tender. Drain and mash well. Beat in butter, salmon and half of the drained Niblets. Season well with salt and pepper. Spread mixture on a plate. Refrigerate until cold.

Meanwhile, make sauce, gently fry onion in the oil for 2-3 minutes, until softened. Add the tomatoes, tomato puree and stock cube. Cover the pan and simmer gently for 15-20 minutes. Stir in remaining Niblets; season well with salt and pepper.

FOLLOW OUR
FASHION A-Z

Confused and muddled when it comes to clothes? Not sure what to look for or how to care for them? Follow our A-Z of fashion — you'll find it full of fun.

A is for apple-pie order and how you should keep your clothes! Hang everything neatly in cupboards and folded up in drawers.

B is for black. It can make you look drab and boring — so go for bright colours instead!

C is for comfortable. Wear shoes and dresses that fit properly. Tight shoes will ruin your feet and you'll look just plain silly in a dress that's two sizes too small. Take your time when trying on clothes and shoes to make sure they fit.

D is for dress-sense — something well worth having! Keep an eye on what's fashionable and work out exactly what you think will suit you. Get Mum or an older sister to help you sort out which colours you look best in.

E is for effort. Looking good is something that can't be achieved overnight! You have to work at it.

F is for finance. Make sure yours are in good order before going out on a shopping spree. If not, start saving those pennies now!

G is for green — a colour some say is unlucky. Take no notice — on the right people it can look terrific. In the summer it can make you appear cool, even if you're not!

H is for holiday — a time when you should look extra smart. Plan that fun-time away wardrobe with extra care. Make a list of what you'll need but don't overpack.

I is for impact — just what you want to create when you walk down the street! Don't be afraid to be seen in striking clothes. Not only will you cheer yourself up, but you'll cheer everyone else up too!

J is for jumper — make sure you have one to keep you warm on cold days. You can always just throw it round your shoulders if it gets a bit on the chilly side!

K is for knitting — why not get someone to show you how? You'll save money when it comes to buying woolly things!

L is for label. Always check the label in something before you buy it — not only for size and price, but to see whether it's washable or should be dry-cleaned. No point in buying a white blouse that's always got to be dry-cleaned. It'll work out very expensive!

M is for Mum — who should be your very best friend when it comes to buying clothes and helping you decide what's what!

N is for new. Try to keep your clothes looking that way by careful washing and ironing.

O is for ordinary — something you should never look! Choose clothes with care and really hunt around for unusual garments. Jumble sales and Oxfam shops can be a surprising source.

P is for pink — a pretty colour that most people look good in. Try to include at least one pink sweatshirt in your wardrobe.

Q is for quick. Before you go out,

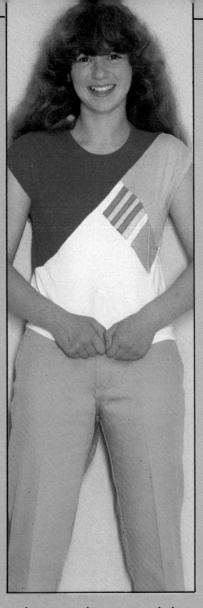

make sure you've got enough time to check your image in the mirror. Don't be in such a hurry!

R is for right — and don't forget the customer always is too! If you buy something that's faulty — like a dress with a zip that busts a week after purchase — don't be afraid to take it back to the shop.

S is for shops. Don't just stick to your favourite few — always seek out new ones! And whatever you do, don't let sales-assistants talk you into buying something you don't really want.

T is for temptation. Don't rush out and spend all your money on something that suddenly catches your eye. Think about it first and decide if you really need it.

U is for underwear. Make sure you always wear a nice pair of briefs and petticoat. All the big chain stores sell lovely stuff.

V is for vest. You can get some very pretty ones tht look very different from Dad's old string number! Wear one when the weather turns a bit nippy!

W is for wear. Make sure you wear everything in your wardrobe! What about that nice dress stuffed right at the back? Get it out and put it on — poor neglected thing!

X is for Xmas. This is the time to try out your new gear and get dressed up to go to parties. Don't overeat too much though, otherwise those zips will stick!

Y is for yellow — always a colour to consider...

Z is for zest — which you should always have and will shine through whatever you're wearing!

It's not just us girls who have to watch our weight, y'know — a lot of our favourite stars have to really work at keeping trim!

CLIFF JOINS THE CLUB

It's funny, 'cos we never think of Cliff as being the old-timer of the pop world, but he is!

"When you get to my age," he says jokingly, "you have to watch out for the old spare tyre developing! I've had a few in my time, I can tell you, but I've found the ideal way to fight the flab, so Terry Wogan — you can eat your heart out!

"I swim. Yes, it really is as simple as that! I find that a quick dip in the pool, a couple of times a day, is all the exercise I need to keep me in shape. And it's a lovely relaxing way to do it after a hard day's work. I usually go first thing in the morning, then again when I get home in the evening.

It is really a good job I don't have to go through gym workouts or anything too energetic or I reckon you'd definitely see a spreading Cliff before too long!"

POLICE AT BAY

You might think that Sting, Stewart and Andy are the last guys in the world to have to worry about their bods — after all, they look just about perfect, don't they?

"Stewart and I don't have any weight problems," Sting admits. "Don't let Andy hear me saying this, but he's the one who has to watch the bathroom scales! It's true — given half a chance, our Andy'd turn into a right old Billy Bunter, but we see to it that he doesn't get the chance. Right, Stu?"

"You bet!" Stewart agrees. "We make him carry all our gear round everywhere we go and the fat just rolls off him!"

Something tells us they're pulling a fast one on poor old Andy — but they'd better beware 'cos he looks as if he's in such good shape now, he'll steal their limelight!

SHEENA SPOTS TROUBLE

Like most Scots girls, Sheena really enjoys her food, so to keep herself in good enough shape for all those super clothes she wears, she has to keep a careful eye on the scales!

"It's not so much putting on weight that's a problem with me," Sheena says, "because I'm so busy, I use up most of the calories in nervous energy! But I do have to watch my skin because nothing looks worse in close-up photographs than a spotty face!

"I try to eat plenty of fresh fruit and vegetables — preferably raw — that way, I feel and look healthy!"

We think she always manages to look pretty amazing!

HAZEL'S HOOKED

One of our favourite stars, Hazel O'Connor, doesn't mind admitting she's always fighting a losing battle against the dreaded flab!

"Ever since I was a kid at school, I've been, shall we say, tending towards the podgy side...It doesn't seem to matter how many diets I try, I always end up stuffing myself with cream cakes and biscuits in desperation after a few days — then it's back to square one! I've been on the strawberry diet (till I was sick of the sight of 'em!), the banana diet, the grapefruit diet — you name it, I've tried it. I'm just waiting for some bright spark to come up with a cream bun diet — then I'm really in with a chance! Till then, I'll have to carry on the way I do now — but I really will take my dog, Sam for more walks and cycle to work more often 'cos the exercise'll do me good."

Cinderella's Dream

While London starts to rise, there are girls who have been up and about for some time . . .

And at that early hour, girls and boys glide, twirl and pirouette on ice as they practise . . . and dream that one day they will skate to stardom.

THAT'S SUPER, CLARE . . .!

YOUNG CLARE'S NOT BAD AT ALL, BUT WHAT'S ALL THE EXCITEMENT ABOUT?

TOMORROW'S A BIG DAY FOR THE GIRLS HERE, ADA.

A MRS. HOWARD IS COMING. SHE'S A TALENT SCOUT FOR A COMPANY THAT'S PUTTING ON A PANTOMIME SOON — **CINDERELLA ON ICE.**

AND, OF COURSE, EVERYONE OF THOSE GIRLS IS HOPING TO BE PICKED FOR A PART.

IT'S HARD FOR HER NOW, BUT ONE DAY SHE'S GOING TO BE RIGHT AT THE TOP — YOU MARK MY WORDS!

A little later . . .

PHEW . . . I'VE NEARLY FINISHED!

I EXPECT YOU CAME OUT WITHOUT ANY BREAKFAST AS USUAL, LOVE.

SO I'VE BROUGHT YOU SOME FRESH CRISP ROLLS AND BUTTER. NOW YOU SIT DOWN A MINUTE WHILE I MAKE A NICE CUP OF TEA.

THANK YOU, MRS. HARRIS

EXCITED ABOUT TOMORROW, LOVE?

OH, WELL, YES, I AM — BUT I DON'T EXPECT I'LL EVEN GET THE CHANCE OF AN AUDITION.

YOU WILL, HEATHER — AND THEY'LL WANT YOU IN THE PANTOMIME.

THAT WOULD BE MARVELLOUS . . .

BUT I'M SURE IT WON'T HAPPEN.

ALL THE SAME, YOU COME ALONG NOW AND LET ME SEE YOU PRACTISE.

A few moments later . . .

CLARE — THERE WAS NO NEED TO DROP THAT LITTER. MRS. HARRIS HAS JUST CLEANED UP HERE!

THEN SHE CAN DO IT AGAIN — THAT'S WHAT SHE'S PAID FOR, ISN'T IT?

OR DO IT YOURSELF — THERE'S NO POINT A SKIVVY LIKE YOU WASTING YOUR TIME TRYING TO SKATE!

DO COME ALONG, DARLING — YOU KNOW WE HAVE TO BUY YOU THAT NEW SKATING DRESS FOR TOMORROW.

TAKE NO NOTICE OF HER, LOVE — IF THE TRUTH WERE KNOWN, SHE'S JUST JEALOUS OF YOU.

NOW YOU FORGET ALL ABOUT THEM AND LET ME SEE HOW WELL YOU CAN SKATE.

Once on the ice, as always, Heather lost herself in her dream world.

I'M A STAR, DANCING OUT HERE ALL ALONE ON THE ICE . . .

DANCING BEFORE A HUGE AUDIENCE . . .

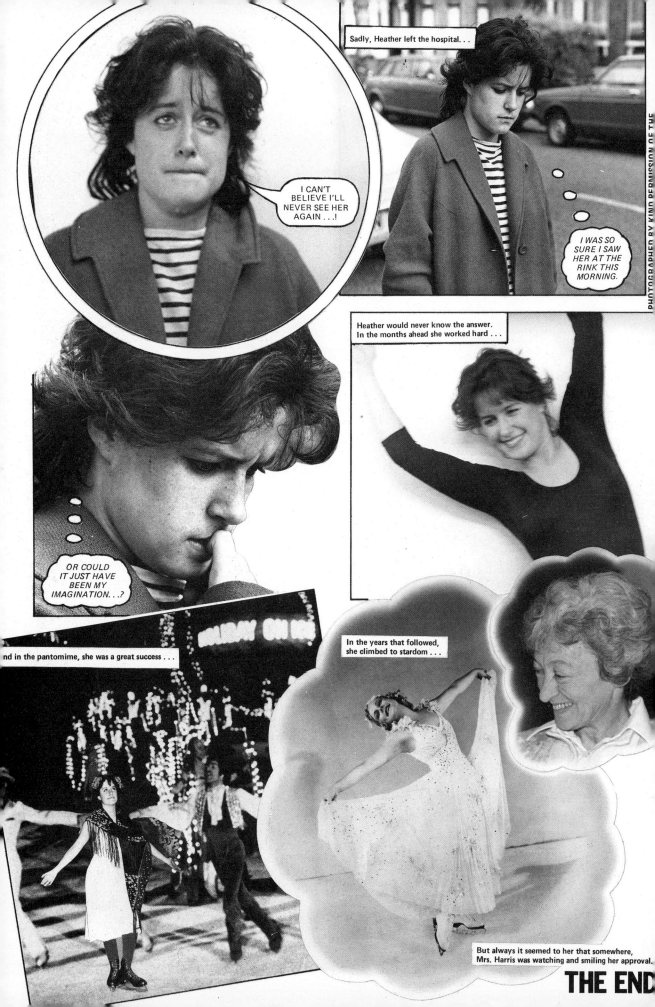

20 Ways To Be Popular...

... Make a point sometimes of putting others first instead of yourself.

... Offer to go shopping or run an errand for Mum — she'll appreciate the thought.

... Take the dog for an extra long walk — it'll do you both good!

... Try not to let your temper get out of control. You'll only regret it later.

... Keep a book of family and friends' birthdays — then you've no excuse for forgetting them!

... Don't gossip about others — then they won't gossip about you.

... Instead of ignoring your kid brother or sister, join in a game with them. You might even enjoy it!

... Visit an elderly person and cheer them up with a chat.

... If your pal does you a good turn, always try and repay the favour.

... Take Mum and Dad a cup of tea in bed on Sunday morning as a special treat.

... Be a good sport and accept defeat graciously.

... And if you win, don't rub it in by being big-headed about your success!

... Don't be a misery. If your friends suggest something you don't want to do, don't just sulk but try suggesting something else instead.

... Remember to be polite. 'Please' and 'thank you' don't cost anything!

... Share sweets with your mates.

... Don't take your parents for granted — think of all the things they've done for you.

... Be a good listener if your friends have problems and never blab their secrets afterwards.

... If you borrow something, always return it as soon as you've finished with it.

... Don't tell tales on your brothers and sisters. And if there's an argument at home or among friends, don't take sides.

... Smile! Everyone likes a happy face!

CUTE 'N' COSY!

That's what these simple knits are ...

PUNCH AND JUDY PUPPETS

MATERIALS 1 × 50 g balls of Hayfield Beaulon DK in each of the following colours — yellow, pink, blue, green, red and white Few yards in royal blue and rust for eyes
1 pair of 4 mm (no. 8) knitting needles

MEASUREMENTS Approx 22 cm tall (excluding hat)

TENSION 11 sts and 14 rows to 5 cm over st st on 4 mm needles

Mr. PUNCH

Main Piece

Using red, cast on 40 sts and work 4 rows in k1, p1 rib.
Cont in st st, working (2 rows green, 6 rows red) 5 times. Break off red and green and join in pink. Work 8 rows.

Shape Head

1st row K2tog, k16, k2 tog, turn and cont on these sts, dec one st at each end of every knit row until 10 sts rem, ending with a k row.
Next row P2 tog, p6, p2 tog.
Next row K2 tog, k4, k2 tog. Cast off.
Rejoin yarn to the other 20 sts and work to match.

Arm

Using red, cast on 3 sts and p 1 row. Cont in st st, inc one st at each end of next and every alt row until there are 17 sts, then cont straight until work measures 6.5 cm from beg, ending with a p row.
Work 2 rows in green and 2 rows in pink.

Shape Hand

1st row With pink, k2 tog, k4, k2 tog tbl, k1, k2 tog, k4, k2 tog tbl.
2nd row P 13
3rd row K2 tog, k2, k2 tog tbl, k1, k2 tog, k2, k2 tog tbl.
4th row P 9
Cast off.

Nose

With pink, cast on 15 sts and work in st st, slipping the first st of every row, and at the same time dec one st at each end of every alt row until 3 sts rem, ending with a p row. K3 tog and fasten off.

Hat

Using green, cast on 40 sts and work 6 rows in garter st. Break off green. Join in red and cont in st st, dec one st at each end of every alt row until 2 sts rem, ending with a p row. K2 tog and fasten off.

Frill

Using white, cast on 120 sts and work 8 rows in k3, p3 rib.
Next row *K3 tog, p3 tog, rep from * to end.

K 1 row, then cast off.

To Make Up

Join seam of arm. Join seam of main piece, inserting arm between the top green stripe and the 3rd green stripe. Make a fringe of yellow hair on the front of the hat, then join seam of hat and sew hat to head. Make a small pom-pom in green and sew to top of hat. Join seam of nose and sew on nose. Embroider eyes, eyebrows and mouth. Join frill into a circle and stitch round neck.

JUDY

Main Piece and Arm

Work as given for Mr. Punch, but using blue instead of red and green.

Apron

Using white, cast on 30 sts and work 4 rows in g st, 2 rows in st st, 4 rows in moss st and 14 rows in st st.
Next row K2 tog to end. 15 sts.
Next row Cast on 50 sts, work in moss st to end.
Rep the last row once more. 115 sts. Work 2 rows in moss st. Cast off.

Hat

Using white, cast on 120 sts, work 2 rows in st st, 4 rows in moss st, then 2 rows in st st.
Next row K3 tog to end. 40 sts.
P 1 row, work 5 rows in moss st, then p 1 row.

Next row K2 tog to end. Next row P. Rep the last 2 rows twice more. 5 sts. Break off yarn, thread through sts, draw up and fasten off, leaving an end of yarn to join seam.

To Make Up
Join arm and main pieces as for Mr. Punch, placing arm between 17th and 32nd rows of main part. Cut strands of yellow approx 25cm long for hair. Place over head and stitch along centre to denote parting. Tie strands tog at back and stitch lightly to back of neck. Embroider eyes and mouth. Join seam of hat *and stitch hat in place. Stitch apron to body at front, tie ends at back.

* Make a plait in pink, blue and yellow and thread through the 'k3 tog' row of hat.

HOT WATER BOTTLE COVERS

MATERIALS Owl: 2 × 50g balls of Hayfield Beaulon DK in cream
Oddments in burnt brown, colwyn and rust

Mouse: 2 balls in burnt brown Oddments in colwyn and shrimp 1 pair of 4mm (no. 8) knitting needles

MEASUREMENTS 21 cm wide and 31 cm high (excluding ears)
This will fit a child's standard hot water bottle

TENSION 11 sts and 14 rows to 5cm over st st on 4mm needles

OWL

Main Pieces (Make 2)
Using cream, cast on 38 sts and work 2 rows in st st.
Cont in st st, inc one st at each end of next and every alt row until there are 46 sts, then cont without shaping until work measures 21 cm from beg, ending with a p row.
Cast off 4 sts at beg of next 6 rows. Work 20 rows straight, then dec one st at each end of next 4 rows. Cast off.

To Make Up
Following the chart, Swiss darn wings & breast feathers on front. Embroider claws at bottom of front.
Embroider eyes, using a circle of chain stitch in centre, then a circle of straight stitches, with a row of blanket stitch outside. Using brown, embroider nose between the eyes, using satin stitch or straight stitches.
Join the two pieces, leaving an opening at top for filling bottle.
Insert hot water bottle from the bottom and join seam.

MOUSE

Main Pieces (Make 2)
Work as given for Owl, but working in burnt brown.

Tummy
Using colwyn, cast on 16 sts and work in st st, inc one st at each end of every alt row until there are 22 sts. Work 20 rows straight, then dec one st at each end of every alt row until 16 sts rem. Cast off.

Ears (Make 2 in burnt brown and 2 in shrimp)
Cast on 17 sts and work 16 rows in st st, dec one st at each end of every alt row until 9 sts rem. Cast off.

Tail
Using burnt brown, cast on 60 sts and work 6 rows in st st. Cast off loosely.

To Make Up
Sew tummy to front. Embroider eyes and nose in chain stitch and whiskers in long straight stitches. Fold tail in half lengthwise, with the purl side outside and join seam.
Join pieces as for Owl. Stitch ears together in pairs (one brown and one pink in each pair), gather lower edges of ears and stitch to top of head at each side of opening, with the pink side to the front. Sew tail to bottom of back.

HOUSE TEA-COSY

MATERIALS 2 × 50g balls of Hayfield Beaulon DK in sunshine
2 balls in pink
Oddments in colours as required for embroidery
1 pair of 4mm (no. 8) knitting needles
Piece of quilting, wadding or other flat filling 30cm × 42cm

MEASUREMENTS 33 cm wide and 22 cm high (approx)

TENSION 11 sts and 14 rows to 5cm over st st on 4mm needles

Using sunshine, cast on 77 sts and work in st st, work 28 rows in sunshine, 84 rows in pink, 56 rows in sunshine, 84 rows in pink, then 28 rows in sunshine. Cast off.

X Brown   O Colwyn   ● Rust

THE PET SHOP

Girl

Caring For Your Pet

Quaker have produced a super 12-page illustrated booklet for people who have a dog or cat at home, called 'Caring For Your Pet'.

If you'd like a free copy, write, enclosing a smallish stamped, self-addressed envelope, to: Pet Booklet Dept. (Girl), RHA — 7 High Street, Maidenhead, Berkshire. (Quaker are the people who make 'Chunky' dog food and 'Felix' cat food.)

The booklet tells you how to give your dog or cat the best possible care and attention. Here are some pet care queries, which have been answered by the Quaker Petcare consultant. Hope you find the answers helpful.

Don't forget to send us a picture of your pet. And remember to drop us a line telling us a little bit about him or her ...

TOOTHACHE?

Do animals get toothache like humans do?

Lisa, Southend.

Quaker reply: Yes, check your pet's teeth and gums occasionally for decay and infection. Older animals sometimes suffer from sore gums and may need softer food; or decayed teeth which cause pain, loss of condition and bad breath. Bad teeth should be removed by your vet or at a pet clinic.

BATH TIME

My dog has short hair and doesn't get dirty. Should I still bath him occasionally?

Susan, Manchester.

Quaker reply: Yes, an occasional bath in your kitchen sink or the bath, or in summertime, use a tub in the garden — will keep your dog clean and sweet-smelling. Use a dog shampoo and always make sure he is thoroughly dry afterwards, especially underneath. Use a clean towel — and if he has long hair, finish drying him with a hair-dryer.

KITTY CARE

Daddy has bought me a kitten, and I'd like him to sleep in my bedroom, but Mummy says, 'No'. Why not? It's not fair!

I just can't see why it would be wrong. Surely she's being unreasonable — don't you agree?

Jane, Berkshire.

Quaker reply: It is best for kittens to get used to sleeping quietly, by themselves, at night. As he gets older, your cat may want to go out after dark, through a cat-door or small window left open for him. Kittens love warmth and security. Provide a box or basket with a soft blanket, and put him in a quiet corner near heat, like a radiator.

So, what's it like to be at Stage School?

We spent the day finding out especially for you ...

You may have wondered where we get the girls who appear on the cover of *Girl* every week ...

Well, a lot of them come from stage schools in London. We have to restrict it to the London area because the photographer's studio is based in London and that's where we take the photographs.

So do these girls spend their time having their photographs taken every day?

SCHOOL WORK

No, not at all. Their days are split up between school work and stage work. This includes ballet, tap, singing, dancing, mime and acting. The girls all wear a school uniform both for their school work and other subjects.

Each year, all the girls and boys have their photographs in the school model book. This gets distributed to people wanting young models.

AUDITIONS!

Once somebody has selected a face or faces that they like the look of, the girls or boys are asked to go along for an audition.

This can be very nerve-racking when you know that there are so many people there all after the same job as you!

BOOKINGS

The school provides a chaperone who takes you along to your audition. This is to make sure you don't have any problems finding the place, then the chaperone waits whilst the audition takes place. After the audition's over, you're ready to go home.

Some of the most popular bookings which come along are for commercials and telly serials, but it's all a lot of hard work.

Another thing is, stage schools tend to have much shorter holidays than ordinary schools.

And don't think that school work takes second place though, because it doesn't! This is a very important part of the course. Girls and boys take exams and work towards 'O' and 'A' levels just like any ordinary school.

QUALIFICATIONS

In fact, everyone is encouraged to get as many qualifications as possible because at the end of the day, when you're ready to leave school and go to work, there are not that many jobs available in TV, films or the theatre. So you see, you have to be prepared to choose a different career.

Not a very pleasant fact, you might think, but it's true, and everyone is taught that this is what could easily happen to them at the end of the day.

After all, it's not often that a new star is born, is it?

CUTE 'N' COSY KNITTING
Continued from page 75

To Make Up

Fold both ends to the middle and join the side seams. Insert wadding, putting half into each end, then join seam in centre. With the seam to the inside, fold cosy in half and join the sides. Following the charts, work embroidery on back and front of cosy, on the 42 rows of pink. The flowers and leaves are worked in Swiss darning, in colours as you like, and the doors, windows and tree tub in satin stitch, working over half a stitch of the knitting. The lines at top and bottom of the doors and windows are worked in Swiss darning.

SWISS DARNING

Thread the yarn into a blunt-ended sewing needle and begin at the lower right hand corner of the motif to be embroidered. Bring the needle through at the base of the first stitch to be worked from the back to the front and draw the yarn through. Insert the needle from right to left, under the two loops of the same stitch one row above and draw the yarn through. Insert the needle back into the base of the first stitch and through the base of the next stitch to the left and draw the yarn through.

At the end of the row, insert the needle into the base of the last stitch worked then up into the centre of this same stitch, which will be the base of the same stitch on the next row above. Insert the needle from left to right behind the two loops of this stitch on the row above and continue working as before, from left to right.

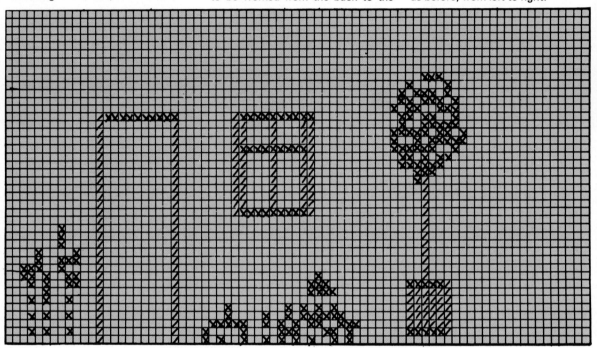

X Swiss Darning   / Satin Stitch

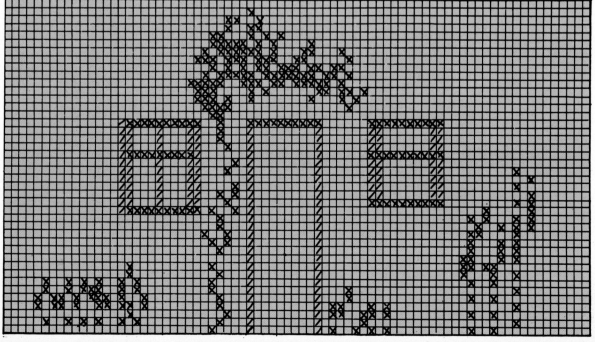

So You Want To Be a Model...

Here's the low-down from a young model on just what the modelling game is all about!

They look pretty glamorous, don't they — those pretty girls in glossy magazines, modelling all those fantastic clothes?

And probably, like the great majority of people, you think they lead a glamorous life too, rushing around to photographers' studios, wearing super outfits and meeting lots of exciting people.

Bet you've even thought about becoming a model yourself, haven't you? Come on, admit it!

PRETTY!

Most girls have at some stage — especially if they are at all pretty!

But is it all that it seems?

We spoke to Vicki, a young and very pretty model at a leading London agency and asked her just what she thought about modelling as a career.

"It's pretty tough," she admitted. "Modelling's certainly not the glamorous job most people expect it to be. I have to keep myself in tip-top condition all the time. My hair and skin have to look perfect and I daren't put on an ounce of weight!

BORING

"It can be a real bore when friends ask you out for the evening. There's no way you can gorge yourself on burgers and huge pieces of sticky cake.

"The chances are, you'll be out in a rash of spots the next day — not funny if you're going to be photographed close-up!

EARLY NIGHTS!

"I also have to make sure I have plenty of early nights. I can't afford to look tired."

Vicki also told us there was a lot of competition. "It's about the most competitive job around! I was lucky. I just went along to an agency and they liked me. Yet thousands of pretty girls don't make it — they get rejected by all the agencies.

"Having an agent is vital. You have to have someone who's in daily contact with magazines and photographers. They get all the jobs in and find you work."

Is the money all that fantastic?

"Some weeks I make quite a bit, but other weeks I may only earn a few pounds if there's not that much work about."

So why does she do it?

"It's different. I'm not mad about working in an office. I do get out and about, and meet people.

TRIPS

"I've also been abroad on trips, photographing clothes for catalogues which is hard work, but great fun. I'd never have been able to visit places like America or North Africa if it wasn't for my modelling career."

And does Vicki intend to carry on with it?

"Until my looks start fading — this is hardly a job I can do all my life! But perhaps in a few years time, I might even start up my own model agency. Who knows?"

We wish you luck, Vicki!

Birthday Bonanza
Seeing Stars!

Find out the date of your favourite person's birthday. It might even be the same day as your own.

ARIES

March 24th — Peter Powell
March 26th — Diana Ross

TAURUS

April 25th — Bjorn from Abba
May 7th — Richard O'Sullivan

GEMINI

June 3rd — Suzi Quatro
June 18th — Paul McCartney

CANCER

July 12th — Cheryl Ladd
July 23rd — David Essex

LEO

July 30th — Kate Bush
August 20th — Phil Lynott

VIRGO

August 27th — John Lloyd
September 1st — Barry Gibb

LIBRA

October 2nd — Sting
October 14th — Cliff Richard

SCORPIO

November 14th — Prince Charles
November 15th — Frida from Abba

SAGITTARIUS

December 11th — Rita Ray from Darts
December 3rd — Paul Nicholas

CAPRICORN

December 23rd — Rod Stewart

AQUARIUS

February 18th — John Travolta

PISCES

February 24th — Dennis Waterman
March 4th — Shakin' Stevens

80

POSTBOX

DARLING DAD

The other night, all the family were sitting glued to the telly when Dad announced he was feeling hungry and went into the kitchen.

He was in the process of making a cheese sandwich when he noticed a green slimy thing on the draining board.

Timidly, he tip-toed towards the cutlery drawer and pulled out a large bread knife. Advancing forward, he made a vicious chop towards this unknown object.

My dad had daringly and bravely killed — a pickled gherkin!

Sally, Glasgow.

TOO CHEAP!

When I was short of money, I went out and bought myself a slightly imperfect pair of tights. They were a lot cheaper than the ones I usually get.

Well, I put the tights on — only to find they had three legs!!

I'll know better next time, won't I?

Sarah, Bristol.

TOOTHY TALES

My dopey big brother went into the bathroom and went through the usual routine of washing. Then it came to brushing his teeth.

He found a tube in the bathroom cabinet, squeezed some of the contents onto his toothbrush and started cleaning his teeth.

He soon stopped though when he found he was using Mum's hair removing cream!

Karen, Huddersfield.

REAL LIVE MEN!

Thought I'd tell you about my mum. She was at a local air-show when she saw some parachutes in the sky and said, 'Oh, look at those toy parachutes up there.'

Was she surprised when Dad told her that they were real men in parachutes.

We haven't let her live it down since!

Melanie, Southampton.

Published by IPC Magazines Ltd., King's Reach Tower, Stamford Street, London SE1 9LS. Sole Agents for Australia and New Zealand: Gordon & Gotch Ltd. South Africa: Central News Agency. Printed in Italy by New Interlitho, S.p.A., Milan. Typeset by Pace Photosetting (London) Ltd.   **SBN 85037 8249**

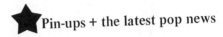

QUICK CHECK

How did you get on with our bumper crossword? Check out the answer here!

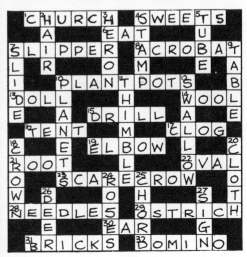

Rhona's rocketing shot gave the keeper no chance

I'VE DONE IT! I — I'VE DONE IT!

It was the only goal of the match, and when the final whistle blew...

WE'RE THROUGH TO THE QUARTER-FINALS, THANKS TO YOU!

WELL PLAYED, RHONA!

THANKS, BUT I'M ONLY PART OF A TEAM. THE OTHERS DID THEIR BIT, TOO!

On the way home —

HEY, WHAT'S WRONG?

NOTHING, SNIFF — I'M JUST SO HAPPY — YOU WERE RIGHT, HELEN, NOW THAT HORRID DOLL'S GONE, EVERYTHING'S OKAY!

IT'S GREAT TO BE MY OLD SELF AGAIN. FUNNY, I — I'VE SUDDENLY GOT A FEELING THERE'S SOMETHING I MUST DO!

Almost in a daze, Rhona took a chair to the cupboard and stood on it —

WHAT COULD IT BE — I DON'T KEEP THINGS ON TOP OF THE CUPBOARD?

OH NO — IT'S THAT DOLL — AND...AND ITS EYES ARE OPEN AGAIN!

I DON'T KNOW HOW, BUT IT SEEMS TO BE THE CAUSE OF ALL MY TROUBLES.

OH NO — I'M TOO LATE! MY — MY HEAD IS SPINNING AGAIN — I'M GOING TO GET ANOTHER HORRIBLE BLACKOUT AND DO STUPID THINGS...

A-AND I'M GETTING THOSE VISIONS — WHAT CAN THEY MEAN?

Seconds later —

GOOD. THERE IS NO PAIN NOW.

I'LL PUT IT BACK IN THAT BOX. IT IS SAFE THERE.

NOW I MUST MAKE PREPARATIONS FOR THE MORNING. IT WILL BE GOOD TO GO HOME!

ARE YOU GOING OUT AGAIN, RHONA?... RHONA?

THAT'S FUNNY, RHONA INVITED ME ROUND TO LISTEN TO HER NEW LP, BUT SHE'S GOING OUT!

HEY, RHONA — YOU FORGOTTEN ABOUT THIS EVENING?

SHE LOOKS STRANGE. OH CRUMBS, SHE'S SEEN ME AND RUN OFF. PERHAPS SHE'S GOT ONE OF THOSE TURNS AGAIN — I'D BETTER KEEP AN EYE ON HER!

FLAMING RUSH-HOURS — YOU CAN NEVER GET ACROSS THIS ROAD!

And by the time Helen did get across —

OH, NO! I'VE LOST HER! SHE WAS ALRIGHT EARLIER. I CAN'T UNDERSTAND — WAIT.... SOMEHOW THAT DOLL MUST'VE TURNED UP AGAIN!

I WISH TO GET TO STONEHENGE.

SIMPLE, LOVE. THIS ROAD GOES THROUGH SALISBURY PLAIN — THE HENGE IS ABOUT THREE-QUARTERS OF A MILE, ON YOUR LEFT.

THERE IS NO TIME TO BE LOST.

BAH, THE MANNERS OF THE MODERN GENERATION — NOT EVEN A "THANK YOU" !

About fifteen minutes later —

AH YES. I REMEMBER IT NOW FROM WHEN I ARRIVED.

THERE IS THE LANDING PLATFORM — "ALTAR STONE" I BELIEVE EARTH PEOPLE CALL IT FOR SOME REASON.

I MUST COMPUTE THE APPROACH ANGLE FOR THE SHUTTLE CRAFT FROM MY OWN PLANET. IT IS TO RESCUE ME NEXT TIME THE EARTH SUN RISES.

OOH. THIS EARTHLET'S BODY IS SO LARGE, IT IS DIFFICULT TO CONTROL.

TO THINK THEY BELIEVE MY RACE TO BE NOTHING BUT DOLLS, WE ARE SMALL COMPARED WITH THEM, BUT THEIR BRAINS ARE PUNY COMPARED WITH OUR KNOWLEDGE AND INTELLECT !

WHAT A PITY MY OWN BODY CANNOT LIVE IN THE EARTH'S ATMOSPHERE. THE CRIPPLED SHUTTLE-CRAFT HAD TO USE ITS RAY TO PUT ME IN A STATE OF SUSPENDED-ANIMATION SO THAT I MIGHT SURVIVE UNTIL IT RETURNED.

TCH ! WHAT RUDENESS !

IT IS FORTUNATE THAT SILLY GIRL, RHONA, FOUND ME, SO THAT I AM ABLE TO TAKE OVER HER BODY WHEN I WISH, AND REGAIN MY FREEDOM !

BUT I SHALL HAVE TO RETURN SOON TO MY OWN BODY, AND TRANSMIT MY INFORMATION BY THOUGHT TO THE COMMANDER. ANYWAY, I CAN ONLY REMAIN OUTSIDE OF IT FOR TWELVE HOURS OR I WOULD DIE, SO TOO, WOULD THAT RHONA!

'ERE WOTCH IT — PUSHIN' US AROUND JUST 'COS YOU'RE BIG!

BUT WITH MY SUPERIOR MIND, I CAN WILL THAT STUPID RHONA TO STAY NEAR SO THAT I CAN USE HER TO BRING MY REAL BODY TO THE LANDING STONE BY DAWN!

But, back at Rhona's home, the alien's plans were about to be upset —

THESE CURTAINS JUST WON'T HANG PROPERLY SINCE I WASHED THEM. HAVE YOU GOT A DRAWING PIN IN YOUR SATCHEL, TIM?

NO. SORRY, MUM.

BUT THERE'D BE ONE IN THE BOX WITH THE CHRISTMAS GARLANDS. THEY'RE ON TOP OF RHONA'S WARDROBE, I THINK.

OF COURSE! I'LL GO AND BORROW ONE.

SOMEONE HAS LEFT A CHAIR IN FRONT OF THE WARDROBE. THAT'S HANDY.

THIS IS THE BOX. . .WHY, THERE'S THAT HORRIBLE DOLL SHE FOUND!

BRR, IT FEELS ALMOST LIKE COLD FLESH. I'M NOT SURPRISED WE'VE HAD NO LUCK SINCE RHONA BROUGHT IT HOME.

I'LL GET RID OF IT WHILE SHE'S OUT. SHE OBVIOUSLY DOESN'T LIKE IT MUCH, OR IT WOULDN'T BE TUCKED AWAY LIKE THIS.

WHAT HAVE YOU GOT THERE?

IT'S THAT DOLL RHONA FOUND. I'M SENDING IT TO YOUR COUSIN IN SCOTLAND, SHE'S QUITE A SCIENCE-FICTION FREAK, AND I'M SURE THIS'LL THRILL HER TO PIECES!

SEE IF YOU CAN FIND ME A CARDBOARD BOX, TIM, AND WE'LL STRIKE WHILE THE IRON'S HOT. OH, AND SOME BROWN PAPER AND STRING.

RIGHT, MUM. URK, GIVES ME A FUNNY FEELING JUST LOOKING AT IT!

THIS IS THE ONLY ONE I COULD FIND... IT'S A BIT BIG, I'M AFRAID.

ALL THE BETTER! WE CAN STUFF IT WITH NEWSPAPERS AND IT WILL STOP THE DOLL GETTING BROKEN.

Later —

HI! MUM'S GONE OUT TO POST... HUH! SNOOTY, AREN'T WE TODAY?

IT'S GONE — SOMEONE HAS TAKEN IT!

I FEEL THAT HORRID LITTLE BOY KNOWS SOMETHING ABOUT IT!

MY REAL BODY — THAT "DOLL" AS YOU CALL IT — WHERE IS IT? WHAT HAVE YOU DONE WITH IT?

HEY, LAY OFF, SIS!

TELL ME YOU...YOU NASTY CREATURE!

AGH, LEGGO! MUM'S GONE OUT TO POST IT TO KYRA IN SCOTLAND!

THE STUPID WOMAN... THE FOOL!

WAAH!

SHE HAS KILLED ME — AND HER PRECIOUS DAUGHTER!

BLIMEY — SHE'S FLIPPED!

86

BOTH THE EARTH GIRL AND I WILL DIE IF I CANNOT RETURN TO MY OWN BODY. AH, THERE IS FIONA'S MOTHER!

E. FRITO??

THE PACKAGE – WHERE IS IT? YOU WILL TELL ME NOW!

THE POST OFFICE WAS CLOSED SO I SENT IT BY RAIL . . . WHAT'S WRONG, RHONA – YOU LOOK SO STRANGE!

DO NOT HINDER ME. I MUST SOMEHOW RETRIEVE IT!

A PACKAGE FOR SCOTLAND? HMM, IT WOULD HAVE TO GO VIA NEWLAND CITY. SHOULD BE IN THE GUARD'S VAN OF THAT TRAIN. . .

STAND AWAY, THERE!

DON'T, MISS, YOU'LL KILL YOURSELF!

I DO NOT KNOW HOW TO ENTER THIS PRIMITIVE VEHICLE!

CRAZY KID – WHAT'S SHE PLAYING AT?

COME ON, LASS – I'LL GIVE YOU A HAND!

STUPID KID!

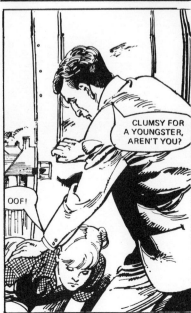

CLUMSY FOR A YOUNGSTER, AREN'T YOU?

OOF!

As soon as she had recovered...

DOES THIS LEAD TO THE, ER... GUARD'S VAN?

HOW SHOULD I KNOW? I'M ONLY A PASSENGER!

YES, THAT IS THE PACKAGE WHICH CONTAINS MY REAL BODY... I SENSE IT!

HEY, WHAT ARE YOU UP TO?

COME BACK... OOF! STOP — THIEF!

I'LL GET YOU! YOU CAN'T GET AWAY!

AH, THAT IS WHAT I NEED TO STOP THIS CRAFT.

UGH — WHAT A VIOLENT HALT. THESE PRIMITIVES HAVE NOT YET DISCOVERED RETRO-HALTERS!

SCREECH

YOU'LL BREAK YOUR NECK, YOU LITTLE NANA!

ARRRRGH!

WELL I AIN'T JUMPING DOWN THERE. I'LL REPORT HER AT THE NEXT STATION, AND LET THE POLICE HANDLE IT!

AGH. I-I CANNOT MAINTAIN AN UPRIGHT POSITION WITH THIS UNWIELDY BODY!

OH – AND IT CAUSES ME **PAIN**. SOB! I MUST GET BACK INTO MY OWN BODY UNTIL IT GOES OFF! IT IS SOMETHING WE NEVER EXPERIENCE IN MY OWN WORLD.

A FEW HOURS SHOULD DO IT. THEN I WILL USE RHONA'S BODY AGAIN TO TAKE MY REAL SELF TO THE LANDING SITE READY FOR THE RESCUE SHIP TO PICK ME UP. HOW I LONG TO LEAVE THIS DISGUSTING PLANET!

CLICK!

With the alien back in her own body, Rhona came to —

MY HEAD! IT'S ACHING AGAIN! I-I MUST HAVE HAD ANOTHER OF THOSE BLACKOUTS!

I REMEMBER NOW! I FOUND THAT HORRID DOLL ON TOP OF MY WARDROBE – THEN I MUST HAVE BLACKED-OUT AND –

HECK, WHERE ON EARTH AM I? A-AND MY LEG IS **PAINFUL** – I WONDER WHAT HAPPENED TO ME **THIS TIME**?

MUM MUST HAVE GIVEN ME THIS PARCEL TO POST. I-I CAN'T REMEMBER A THING ABOUT IT, THOUGH!

I CAN'T POST IT LIKE THIS – ANYWAY, THE POST OFFICE WILL BE CLOSED. I MUST FIND MY WAY HOME SOMEHOW, AND REPACK IT . . . MUM MUSN'T KNOW WHAT'S HAPPENED, SHE'D ONLY WORRY!

A BUS TO BALMSBURY WHERE I LIVE – THAT'S LUCKY! GOOD JOB I'VE GOT SOME MONEY IN MY POCKETS. AS SOON AS I GET BACK, I'LL GET RID OF THAT DOLL ONCE AND FOR ALL!

Later, as soon as Rhona got home —

THE DOLL'S GONE! PHEW – THANK GOODNESS FOR THAT. PERHAPS THAT BLACKOUT WAS THE LAST I'LL GET!

BETTER CHECK THERE'S NOTHING BROKEN BEFORE I RE-WRAP MUM'S PARCEL.

OH NO! THAT AWFUL DOLL WAS IN THE PARCEL ALL THE TIME – **AND I'VE BROUGHT IT BACK HOME WITH ME! WILL I NEVER BE FREE OF IT?**

MOTHER MUST HAVE THOUGHT IT EVIL TOO, AND TRIED TO GET RID OF IT. AND I HAVE TO BE TWIT ENOUGH TO BRING THE THING BACK! WHAT SHALL I DO NOW?

ARE YOU IN THERE, RHONA? HELEN'S CALLED TO SEE YOU.

COMING, MUM!

I'LL WRAP THIS UP LATER AND SEND IF OFF LIKE MUM WANTED.

PHEW, THANK GOODNESS YOU'RE ALL RIGHT! YOU WERE ACTING STRANGELY IN THE STREET, I WAS AFRAID YOU'D GOT ANOTHER OF THOSE BLACKOUTS!

I — I HAD.

Rhona told her friend as much as she could remember of what happened.

HMM. I'VE HAD A FEELING FOR SOME TIME THAT YUKKISH DOLL YOU FOUND HAD SOMETHING TO DO WITH ALL YOUR TROUBLES.

AND I'M CERTAIN OF IT NOW!

I — I WISH I'D NEVER FOUND THE THING — IT'S LIKE A CURSE!

IT'S NO GOOD WISHING, CHUM. COME ON — LET'S THINK WHAT TO DO ABOUT IT!

Y — YOU'RE RIGHT! WELL, ONE THING'S FOR SURE — I COULDN'T BRING MYSELF TO DESTROY IT . . . IT SEEMS SOMEHOW ALIVE!

BRR, I KNOW JUST WHAT YOU MEAN!

I KNOW. I'LL TAKE IT WITH ME. IT CAN'T HURT YOU THEN!

THANKS — BUT NO! I DON'T WANT THESE HORRIBLE THINGS HAPPENING TO YOU.

LET'S WRITE DOWN EVERYTHING WE KNOW THAT HAPPENS — THEN PERHAPS WE'LL GET SOME IDEA HOW TO STOP IT.

LET'S SEE . . . FROM WHAT YOU'VE TOLD ME, THE DOLL'S EYES OPEN, AND THEN YOU START TO FEEL GROGGY, AFTER THAT YOU JUST SEE BLACK.

THAT'S RIGHT. AND IT ONLY HAPPENS WHEN I'M NEAR THE DOLL.

I CAN'T THINK OF ANYTHING ELSE.

I'VE JUST REMEMBERED SOMETHING! WHILE I WAS IN ONE OF THOSE FITS OR WHATEVER THEY ARE, I STARTED SCREAMING THAT AN AIR-FRESHENER IN THE KITCHEN WAS CHOKING ME!

I WONDER IF THAT DOLL IS SOMEHOW AFFECTED BY THEM, TOO?

IT'S WORTH A TRY!

I'LL GET A CAN FROM THE KITCHEN AND PUT IT BY THE DOLL.

NO YOU WON'T — THIS IS MY JOB!

DON'T WORRY . . . REMEMBER, I'VE AT LEAST A MINUTE TO GET AWAY FROM THE DOLL BEFORE I GO DIZZY .

OKAY, BUT FOR GOODNESS SAKE, BE CAREFUL!

GULP — OH WELL, HERE GOES NOTHING!

IT . . . ITS EYES HAVE OPENED! I'D BETTER GET OUT OF HERE — IT'S NOT GOING TO WORK!

Click!

W — WHAT? THEY'VE CLOSED AGAIN! PHEW, I'VE DONE IT — I'VE BEATEN THE THING!

CLICK!

I'M GLAD YOUR IDEA WORKED. I'D BETTER GET HOME. WE'LL TALK ABOUT WHAT TO DO WITH THE DOLL TOMORROW — HOW TO GET RID OF IT ONCE AND FOR ALL.

IT'S GETTING LATE, RHONA. I'VE TURNED DOWN YOUR BED, AND OPENED THE WINDOW FOR A WHILE . . .

. . . IT'S MORE HEALTHY THAN USING THIS .

OH NO — THE AIR-FRESHENER. GIVE ME THAT — QUICK!

WHAT'S GOT INTO THE GIRL? SHE'S ACTING SO STRANGELY!

COME AND SIT DOWN A MOMENT, MRS. FRENCH, AND I'LL ... TRY AND EXPLAIN!

THANK GOODNESS ITS EYES ARE STILL CLOSED! BETTER SHUT THE WINDOW SO THAT THE AIR-FRESHENER HAS FULL EFFECT.

GOSH ... IT'S STIFF. OH NO, I'VE DROPPED IT NOW!

OH HECK, IT ... IT'S EYES ARE OPEN! I'D BETTER GET OUT OF HERE OR I'LL BE IN TROUBLE AGAIN!

OUCH! I'VE BEEN MEANING TO SEE TO THAT FLAMING RUG FOR AGES!

ARGH! MY HEAD'S SPINNING ... IT'S HAPPENING TO ME AGAIN!

One minute — that's all it took. The alien was now in control of Rhona's body!

LUCKY THAT SILLY GIRL KNOCKED THAT CHOKING CHEMICAL OUT OF THE WINDOW. IT IS ONLY A FEW HOURS BEFORE THE RESCUE SHIP LANDS. THERE IS NO TIME TO BE LOST!

A little later ...

I ... I CAN HARDLY TAKE IN ALL YOU'VE TOLD ME!

HECK! RHONA'S BEEN GONE A LONG TIME — WE'D BETTER GO AND SEE SHE'S OKAY.

OH NO – SHE'S GONE! AND SO HAS THE DOLL!

THE SPACESHIP FROM MY OWN PLANET WILL LAND AT DAWN AT WHAT THESE EARTH PEOPLE CALL STONEHENGE.

THEN, WHEN THE SHIP'S RAY RELEASES ME, I WILL BE ABLE TO BREATH EARTH'S AIR LONG ENOUGH TO BE RESCUED.

The hours passed and the sun began to rise . . .

CLICK!

IT IS TIME!

A few moments later, Rhona began to feel herself again . . .

OOH, MY HEAD ACHES SO. BUT I MUST TRY TO THINK CLEARLY. THE DOLL HAD OPENED ITS EYES AND . . .

. . . CRICKEY, I'M IN THE MIDDLE OF SALISBURY PLAIN — AND IT'S NEARLY MORNING! BUT HOW DID I GET HERE?

SWOOOOSH

THERE'S THAT DOLL AGAIN. IT HAD SOMETHING TO DO WITH IT, I BET! BUT WHAT'S THAT RAY OF LIGHT?

ARRRGH! IT MOVED!

IT IS GOOD TO USE MY OWN BODY AGAIN. YOURS IS SO CLUMSY!

WHO . . . WHAT ARE YOU?

93

I AM SREWANA OF THE SPACESHIP, OPSILON. I WAS LEFT BEHIND WHEN IT TOOK OFF FOR EMERGENCY REPAIRS. BUT IT IS RETURNING TO RESCUE ME.

THIS CAN'T BE HAPPENING! IT MUST BE ANOTHER OF THOSE WEIRD DREAMS!

NO, YOUR "DREAMS" HAPPENED WHENEVER I TOOK OVER YOUR BODY. WE OF MY PLANET CANNOT BREATH EARTH AIR FOR LONG, SO I NEEDED TO USE YOUR BODY SO THAT I SHOULD SURVIVE. I USED YOU TO REGAIN MY FREEDOM.

WHY, YOU LITTLE HORROR!

KEEP AWAY FROM ME! DON'T HURT ME!

OH, STOP WHINING! I CAN'T THRASH A TINY THING LIKE YOU, MUCH THOUGH YOU DESERVE IT!

TINY MY PEOPLE MAY BE IN BODY, BUT OUR MINDS ARE FAR SUPERIOR TO THOSE OF YOUR RACE. WHY, WE WERE RULING YOUR PLANET BEFORE YOUR ANCESTORS WERE OUT OF THE CRADLE OF CIVILISATION.

"Our people built this place you call Stonehenge as a spaceport..."

"The stones were markers and what you call the altar stone, a landing platform."

"...In some parts of the world we were worshipped as gods by the earth people, who thought our technology was magic."

THEN A COMET COLLIDED WITH THE EARTH, AND THE GASSES IT RELEASED CHANGED THE ATMOSPHERE. THE EARTH PEOPLE WERE ABLE TO ADAPT, BUT WE COULDN'T.

KEEP AWAY FROM ME! DON'T HURT ME!

AH! HERE IS MY SPACESHIP NOW!

IT...IT'S LIKE A TOY!

Published by IPC Magazines Ltd., King's Reach Tower, Stamford Street, London SE1 9LS. Sole Agents for Australia and New Zealand: Gordon & Gotch Ltd. South Africa: Central News Agency. Printed in Italy by New Interlitho, S.p.A., Milan. Typeset by Pace Photosetting (London) Ltd.